LONG LOST COUSINS,
MILLIE L. McGHEE and KRISTY HOOVER SULLIVAN,
J.Edgar Hoover's Claimed Relative!

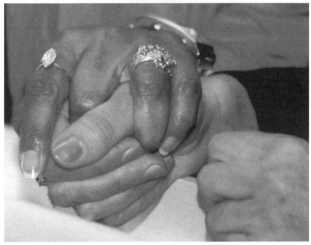

"Holding hands to heal America."
- Millie L. McGhee

"Secrets Uncovered"

J. Edgar Hoover -
The Relative

"There is something addicting about a secret."
- J. Edgar Hoover (1895-1972)

Third Edition
Allen-Morris©
Rancho Cucamonga, CA

Secrets Uncovered, J. Edgar Hoover - The Relative
Copright 2002 by Millie L. McGhee-Morris, Rancho
Cucamonga, California.

**To schedule the author for speaking engagements or to
purchase additional books, please contact:**

Inland Empire Services / Allen-Morris Publishing
Phone: 909-483-0540 - Fax: 909-483-0822
e-mail: big33eagle@aol.com
To order : www.inlandempireservices.com

2 books in one

Millie M.

enjoy

*I dedicate this book
to my loving husband,
Leslie L. Morris, M.D.
and to my family.*

Author: Millie L. McGhee
Cover Design: Ron Kaye & Connie Schmidt
Editor: Allen-Morris©
ISBN: 0-9701822-1-X

CONTENTS

Author's Statement

Sitting here looking back on the writing of Secrets, I knew in my heart that God carried me every step of the way. As a first-time author, I had a lot to learn. I met with some difficult stumbling blocks getting my book to the public.

This edition is a final print, completing my research on the Hoover/Allen family. I knew that I was opening a huge can of worms revealing J. Edgar Hoover's ancestry. I believed that the truth would set me free, but it could also open up a lot of secrets in our family. Except for the strong support and validation from my mother, many family members were skeptical and negative. Some feared that I'd exposed their own secrets without even reading the book.

Before this edition, I spent six years and thousands of dollars to end up with a messy book and a defamed character. I was at an all-time low. I seriously considered giving up on the whole project, until my talk with the spirit of God. On Sunday, November 12, 2000, I went to church and heard a sermon that seemed to be written just for me.

The pastor said, *"Too often, we start things that we never finish. The world is full of unfinished projects. We start and stop when the going gets tough. Don't give up. Keep working toward your goals and dreams. Finish what you start."* I will never forget those words.

The next day, I opened an e-mail to find a letter from a white Hoover cousin. I was getting a lot of crazy e-mails, but in my mind this one was different.

The subject was, *"Hello from Clayton and Julia's Great Granddaughter."* It was written the evening of November 12th.

"To Millie L. McGhee:

If your research is accurate, then we're cousins. Prejudice robbed our ancestors and us of possibilities and connections. I'm proud of you, and thank you for doing the research. If you are ever in the Seattle area, please plan to

visit. It would be great to do a family reunion.
Kristy Hoover Sullivan."

She said more, but that part really got to my soul. I knew this work was important to a family who needed healing and truth. We started e-mailing back and forth. In the spring of 2001, she had a conference in San Diego, CA. and wondered if that was close to where I lived.

I replied, *"I would love to meet you."*

In March, I drove to her hotel in San Diego with agents and a video camera. We talked for hours, and our connection was immediate. We knew we had to be cousins. We looked at pictures, family research, and later reviewed the damages, conspiracy, and character assassination done to stop the book. I told her the horror stories about the attacks on me for writing the book, *"Secrets Uncovered, J. Edgar Hoover Passing For White."* I was amazed at how patient and understanding she was with the whole thing. Though I'd been burned so many times over this book, somehow I knew that I could trust her. She was reaching out to open the skeletons in her family's closet to heal them, as well as help me change racism in the world.

We held hands all the way back to my car, where we took photos and I gave her more copies of my book. It was hard to leave, but I knew this was the start of an important relationship.

When I got home, I called my mother to tell her about our meeting. She was excited, and wanted to meet Kristy, so I took her the next day. It was like a scene from a movie. Mother, and Kristy looked at each other.

Kristy said, *"It's like looking into a mirror."*

Mother replied, *"You look just like Uncle Elb."*

They hugged and kissed. I stood and watched with excitement, and knew we were related.

"Lord Jesus, guide my tongue, and continue to control my heart."   - Millie L. McGhee

FORWARD
McComb, Mississippi Trip!

It gives me great pleasure to give this statement to the readers of the third edition of, *"Secrets Uncovered," J. Edgar Hoover The Relative!"* When reading the first edition, and second edition titled, *"Secrets Uncovered, J. Edgar Hoover Passing For White?"* I knew that there was something more to this story. What African American would pick J. Edgar Hoover as a relative? I wanted to meet this young woman and see what kind of research she had done to come up with such a story.

During my yearlong association with Millie L. McGhee, I finally got a chance to review her work. I read her bio, and found that she was illiterate after graduating high school. The many hours of research and study she put into educating herself, was amazing and exciting. I looked at hours of video tapes, TV and radio interviews, as well as many pictures. The research was done over a period of four years.

It was great to have had the opportunity to travel with her in 2002. We traveled back to Mississippi going through the research that was done there in 2000. A group of us traveled; Millie's newly found cousins, Kristy Hoover Sullivan and her daughter Haley. From Washington DC, Ms. Mertine Moore, an agent; Ms. Denise Boulden, of Seattle, WA, an agent. and police officer; Mr. Wallace Allen, of San Bernardino, CA, a radio talk show host; Mr. Danny Arguello, of Ontario, CA, Vice President of Allen-Morris Publishing; Dr. Leslie L. Morris, Millie's husband; Mrs. Alberta Allen McGhee, her mother; Ms. Queen E. Tobias, her sister; Ms. Heather Kelly, a student photographer of California. However, Dr. Morris took the pictures that are used in this book. We were able to walk on the common burial ground with four generations of ancestors. The burial ground was a part of the plantation. Christian Hoover, a Mississippi Judge, State Legislator, Senator, and Minister once owned this land. Then later the land was willed to Clarence Allen (Big Daddy), Emily Allen's grandson.

It was very interesting to find this history on this white businessman, Mr. Christian (Kit) Hoover. He was laid to rest in the Hoover burial ground not many feet from Ivy Hoover, his African American son, he fathered with Emily Allen. We found this research to be very complex, because of all the erased documents and cover-ups.

The tombstones, Hoover's and Allen's in McComb, MS were side by side. Such a practice of having slaves buried close and adjacent to the master's family is an uncommon situation. This was seldom seen or discovered in the history of genealogy. Normally the slave owners' cemetery plots are distantly separated from their slaves. This unique arrangement was an important highlight of the trip to the Hoover plantation. It added excitement to my work as a genealogist and historian.

I had the privilege of reviewing the census records, wills, vital statistics, reports, and news articles researched by the author. I found the documents clearly understandable in the connection to her newfound white cousin. Conspicuously however, there were no accurate documented records showing how J. Edgar Hoover, a powerful man and Director of the FBI, was a part of the white family he claimed. The oral history spoken to a ten (10) year old girl growing up in McComb, MS seems to fit. The Oral History was accurate, and did match many of the documents found. The lack of accurate birth or death records found by the author showed similar roadblocks for the white Hoover family as well. They were searching for J. Edgar Hoover's roots to substantiate his claim as a relative, although some records were found suspiciously smudged. I recommend this book to historians and families that are looking for family roots. I found this work educational, and inspiring, and hope it will encourage many to find their roots, as it will help America heal its wounds.

Lucius A. Bowser, Genealogist and Historian, AAHGS.

Remarks By: Kristy Hoover Sullivan

Dear Reader,

We were at a family gathering when my brother, Kim plopped the book on the coffee table in front of us.

Kim said, *"Hey, check this out, Secrets Uncovered, J. Edgar Hoover, Passing for White?"*

I reached out as my parents also clambered to get a closer look. Kim's wife Marcy, had found this book through her genealogical research on the net. We were also conducting our own research on J. Edgar Hoover as well. My cousin's wife, Judy had also been doing research, and had corresponded with Millie, so more of our Hoover blanks were being filled in by her research.

While growing up, when asked whether or not we were related to J. Edgar Hoover, my Dad, Harold Hoover, would remark,

"We don't claim any relation."

When we'd pin him down, he would say that we're supposedly third cousins. Just how that relationship connected with names or records, he couldn't say. J. Edgar Hoover's racism, politics, and tactics cast embarrassment on our family name. The thought that he may have been "passing for white" was absolutely intriguing. Perhaps this could explain some of those *"skeletons in the closet"* that Dad's older sister, Elizabeth told us. When we asked questions about our genealogy.

She'd say, *"You don't want to know. Leave those skeletons in the closet."*

My Great Grandfather, Dr. Clayton Hoover was a *"Horse and Buggy"* doctor in Idaho and written up in history books of the region. At the end of his career, he was the administrator of a mental hospital; quite a respected gentleman. It was surprising to me that we had very little history on his family of origin as well. That November day, Mom, Dad, and I were all three trying to get as much as possible from the book, knowing that I had to leave soon to go home. So, I read through the book as fast as I could, because others wanted to get a look.

I found Clayton A. Hoover's name in the book. Seeing my great grandparents' names in this book stirred me to act.

I wrote down the author's e-mail, so that I could write her. Riding on the ferry to Seattle, on my way home, I rehearsed a letter. I wanted to pour out my heart to this long lost cousin, even if she wasn't, I saw this as a way of bringing blacks and whites together. I am learning that finding African American roots is no easy task. My understanding is that just a few years ago, many genealogist started collecting African American data.

The whole idea of our strand of Hoovers with history in Washington, DC having anything to do with slaves, was a difficult concept to swallow. We were naturally skeptical and as far from slavery as we could possibly get.

The likely hood of J. Edgar being employed in the FBI during the Jim Crow era, had there been a thorough background check, would have been next to none. Economics of the times dictated many decisions and deceptions.

Thousands *"Passed"* to put food on the table. Decisions are made every day that have more to do with economics of survival or greed than what is right and just.

I felt compelled to respond to Millie's work because I saw it as an opportunity to be a part of making a better place for our children. Secrets that hide our identity create hatred and misunderstandings. To free our family they need to be exposed. Whether or not DNA proves our connection, Millie and I are here for the same purpose. I believe that healing our planet starts with healing ourselves. We agree in wanting our children to live in a world where the content of their character is more important than the color of their skin. Millie's courage inspired me to do what I could to embrace our common mission. We hope that in turn, we will have inspired you.

- Kristy Lee Hoover Sullivan

Cousins:
Kristy Hoover Sullivan & Millie L. McGhee

African American Historical Research...

The Connection Between the Allen's and the Hoovers!

"J. Edgar Hoover's Father was Ivery Hoover!"

Elizabeth Allen was indeed the daughter of a slave girl, and the mother of Emily Allen. We are totally satisfied with the research. Most black families' history was not recorded. They had to depend on handed down stories.

We were successful in verifying the existence of many records showing individuals reported in our family stories.

We found true documents that were recorded as far back as 1725, revealing our family secrets.

The slave owners, who impregnated my great, great grandmother Emily, were Christian "Kit" Hoover, his son and a man named, Eff McComb. After finishing the research, I understood the connections, and the documents fit.

Big Daddy told me that J. Edgar Hoover was his second cousin and I believe him. He was his Uncle's son. We found the evidence! Now, let's see how it fits by taking a look at the research done from the beginning.

I noticed that the beginning of our recorded lives started with Christian Hoover, a white man. It showed a black girl named Emily Allen, born in about 1840. In my oral handed down stories according to my family, she was actually born in 1834. The census keepers were not always accurate regarding dates and spelling, especially on the coloreds.

The following research will show names, dates, places, and recorded documents found with the help of Lucius Bowser, a Genealogist /Historian, AAHGS., and George Ott of Salt Lake City, Utah, with Heritage Consulting and Services.

Christian Hoover was born in 1797, in South Carolina. He became a wealthy cotton plantation owner of Pike County, Mississippi. He owned over one hundred slaves. My family was part of his collection. He impregnated my great, great grandmother, Emily Allen. Her mother, Elizabeth was sent, sold, or taken to William Hoover in Maryland. We didn't find anything that told us how she got there, but she ended up there.

The recorded records showed that Christian Hoover married Mary Neyland on April 8, 1823. They had twelve children before her death on February 3, 1858. She was fifty-one years old when she died. Those Hoover children were as follows:

Nancy Ann, born in 1845, died in 1846. John, born in 1827, died in 1831. A son with no recorded name, born in 1829. Mary, born in 1830. Margaret, born in 1831. <u>William, born in 1832</u>, died in 1903. Martha, born in 1832, died in 1833. Christian, born in 1835, died in 1864. Emily, born in 1838, died in 1900.

(Who is this Emily Hoover? She has the same name, birth, and death dates close to that of my great, great grandmother Emily Allen.)

Christian (Kit), born in 1840, died in 1870. Julia, born in 1842. Eliza Jane, born in 1848. Eliza was only ten years old when her mother passed away.

Most of his children by Mary Neyland died young; before the age of thirty-one. Only two of them shown on the records lived past fifty. Big Daddy's grandfather was one of them. He fathered six of Emily's children. He died at seventy-one, which was very close to the same age as his father, Christian, who died at the age of seventy-two. Emily Hoover, his daughter, died at age sixty-two. Those two children lived the longest of the twelve.

Christian's wife Mary Neyland died leaving him with three children under nineteen years of age. It was sad that two of her children died before she did.

(It must have been tough losing those children at such an early age.)

We found out that Christian remarried soon after the death of his wife; of thirty-five years. It appeared that he was having an affair with his second wife before the death of his first wife, because they had children together before her death. We found Susannah's children listed in the census during the time Mary was alive.

He married Susannah Sophia Holbrook March 26, 1859 in Louisiana in the New Orleans Parish. It was only one year and one month after the death of Mary. He was sixty-three years old, and she was forty-one.

Their first two children, Elizabeth, born in 1847, and Robert L.H., born in 1853, were born before Mary's death. The records showed that Robert died in 1930. He lived to be seventy-seven. That made him the longest lived male in the family during that time. Their third child was Lewis Rump Hoover, born in 1862. The records didn't show when he died or if he ever married. He seemed to disappear into thin air.

The fourth child was Mary Hoover born in 1864, and she was the last. It was interesting, that he named this child after his first wife. The records didn't show if she ever married or when she died. After Mary's birth, six years later, her father died at the age of seventy-two. Her mother was only forty-six; still a young woman. When Christian passed away he left his young wife with three young children, but he left her in good care. His son William Hoover, my Big Daddy's grandfather, age thirty-six, was left to look after his stepmother and the children. There were 19 children between those two women.

Christian Hoover was noted as a Mississippi Judge, State Legislator, State Senator, and a Minister. He had relatives as well as business acquaintances in Washington, D.C.

He left his legacy and his business to his son William. I was happy to find out all about Christian through research.

Before the research, I only knew about a slave owner named Hoover, who bought Mama Elizabeth Allen, my third generation great grandmother. I also knew about her daughter Emily Allen, who was J. Edgar's grandmother. Emily had seven children carrying her surname, and one carried the Hoover surname. That was Ivery Hoover, J. Edgar Hoover's biological father. This was part of my Oral History.

I noticed in the research a woman named Elizabeth A. married to a William Hoover. I thought she might be my third generation grandmother, Elizabeth Allen. She was impregnated by William Hoover who was born in 1804 in Maryland.

Elizabeth Allen was born in 1814, in Virginia and taken to Maryland. She gave birth to her daughter Emily Allen in 1834. During the research, I found that some of the dates were estimated. The history that was passed down to me, I believe was correct, because it was told to each generation over and over again.

William Hoover, who was born in 1832, the son of Christian, fathered six of Emily's children. Eff McComb was the father of one, but she was given the Allen surname. Then another child was fathered by Christian, and given the Hoover surname. That child was Ivery Hoover.

I noticed there were many sons named William. I needed to use birth dates when referring to them. In our family a William Hoover was born in 1804, 1832, 1855, and 1863. The William who was born in 1832, married Martha Leticia Jane Thompson. They married on July 27, 1852, had nine children; and he had six by Emily Allen the slave girl.

William was having children by his wife; at the same time he was impregnating Emily Allen. There was a pattern of names passed down through generations. It held true in 1853 when the first child was born with Martha as the mother. They named him Christian R. Hoover, after William's father. The second child by his wife was Thomas Y. Hoover, born in 1855. Then Emily gave birth to her first child, who was not fathered by William, but by Eff McComb. This child was named Malinda Allen, born in 1860. In 1861 a third child was born to his wife Martha, and named William Jefferson Hoover. A second child was born to Emily. Her first son was fathered by Christian Hoover, William's father. This was the only child by Emily that was given the Hoover surname, because he was born on his father's birthday. They named him Ivery Hoover.

William continued his yearly pattern. In 1862 Emily gave birth to a third child, Simon Allen, fathered by him. In 1863 his wife gave birth to a fourth child, Robert M. Hoover. Soon came the fourth child that was born in 1864, by Emily, and named Ebenezer Allen. A year later his wife give birth to Mattie A. Hoover in 1865, which was his fifth child.

He then impregnated them both almost at the same time. His wife gave birth to a sixth, John Stewart Hoover in 1868. Emily gave birth to Lizzie Allen also in 1868, and that made her fifth child at this time. The next year his wife gave birth to Diotician A. Hoover, his seventh child. The year 1870 was an important year in my family's history. Emily gave birth to William Allen, my great, grandfather, Big Daddy's father. He was William Hoover's sixth child with Emily.

In viewing this research, I felt that William Hoover was beside himself. The next time he impregnated them both. His wife's eighth child was Dorthy Virginia Hoover born in 1872. Emily also gave birth to Harrison Allen, her seventh child born in the same year. By this time fourteen children were born, and fathered by William Hoover. Then it seemed William got tired, and took a rest for a while. He didn't impregnate either of them for two years.

In 1875 he resumed his prolific pattern, and impregnated them both again. His wife gave birth to Alvan Wheat Hoover, her ninth child. Emily gave birth to Walter Allen, her eighth child fathered by William. He had fathered fifteen of the seventeen children born at this point in time.

(I wondered if those ladies were aware of each other's pregnancies. I believe they were.)

Back in those days men did whatever they wanted to do, and wives were afraid to say anything. Some white women were treated like slaves as well. It surprised me when mother told me that Emily lived on the plantation.

In the census Emily was listed as William's wife, but he was still married to Martha and having children by them both.

(In my mind I thought that these women cared a lot about each other. I believed that William loved Emily, because they stayed together until death.)

We found information in the 1900 census showing that Martha finally divorced him and moved to Texas, where she died at the age of eighty-two on September 18, 1916. William died January 14, 1903, at the age of seventy-one. The records showed Emily Allen died about 1900.

(I was impressed with how long Martha and Emily lived after having so many babies, and so close together. They were having a baby every year for about eight years.)

I noticed that the life span of their children was longer. Susannah Sophia Hoover, died November 26, 1908, at ninety years old. She outlived her stepson.

Now we are going to take a look at what we found in the research about my Big Daddy and his family. I was so excited when we found my Big Daddy's signature on his Army papers in the census library in Salt Lake City. He was in his early twenties. We also found his marriage certificate, showing he was married to Litta Neal. Her name was changed somewhere in time to Lydia. So, we called her Big Mama Lydia.

Clarence Allen (Big Daddy), and Litta were married on December 23 1915. Rev. W. M. Campbell performed the ceremony. The witnesses were Big Daddy's sister Florence and J. M. Holmes. Clarence and Lydia had sixteen children and my mother was one of them.

We found copies of other family members' marriage certificates, pictures of Big Daddy, his sisters, and his father. There were family records of William Allen, born in February of 1870. He married Elizabeth Haynes, born in November of 1870. I felt proud, because I was born in November myself. They had three children, born in Pike County, Mississippi. My Big Daddy was their first child. In the family group record he was listed as Clarence Allen, born April 9, 1893.

(It was so exciting to see his name, birth date, and his place of birth accurately recorded.)

Their second child, Florence Allen was born in 1894.

(My mother said that when she died, she was giving birth. We found her death record that stated, she indeed died of complications in child birth.)

Their third child, Rosa Allen was born in 1896. Our Oral History was documented in the records as it was told to us.

I read a book written by Curt Gentry entitled "J. Edgar Hoover: The Man and The Secrets." In this book I read about a William Allen in Washington, DC, who worked for the FBI. Then in the same book I noticed that there were two other interesting names. They were family names; Robert Hoover and George Allen. Relatives? Maybe! J. Edgar Hoover had a sister named Lillian Hoover. That is the name of an aunt. She still lives in McComb, Mississippi. J. Edgar Hoover's family connections were so much like those of my family.

In the research we found on Ivy Hoover, some documents were spelled Ivory, Ivery, and Ivy. Ivery Hoover and William Allen, my Big Daddy's father, were very close and more like best friends than brothers, I was told.

Ivery married Arie, (in some documents spelled Ary) in 1879. Arie gave birth to her first child, Earnest J., born in August 1881.

The second child was Eugene E., born in February 1883. The third was Chancy, born in February 1885. It was exciting to find the records of Chancy's marriage, because relatives spoke of him. The marriage certificate showed that he married a lady named Hattie Cockerham on February 23, 1913. They were married in Pike Co., Mississippi.

Uncle Ivery was just as good looking as his father; handsome and tall, so they said. There were rumors that he was quite the ladies man. Family Oral History states that he is J. Edgar Hoover's father. They called him, "An outside child."

I heard the old people say that all the boys were very good looking men. The girls were just as pretty, and they all looked white just like old man Hoover.

Ivery's fourth child Marcenia was born in October 1886. He married Mattie Cockrum. I remember laughing when we found him in the census records. He was listed as Marcenia, a female. We thought it was a girl until we found the family group records.

The fifth child was Chris, named after his father. He was born in June 1887. I noticed that Ivery still hadn't had any girls.

(I knew nothing at all about his children until I did the family research. This is what made the research so exciting. I

didn't know any of these facts, and now it seems like I really know my family better.)

Their sixth child was finally a girl, Clementine, born in December 1892. She married Silas Harris in July 1911. Another girl Mozilla, was born in May 1896, and died at the age of thirty one. She was Ivery's seventh child. Ivery was getting his wife pregnant every year in sequence with the family patterns.

(In 1895, the year J. Edgar was born, she didn't have a child).

I started to understand why Mozilla, told her daughter Louise, about her father. She told them about Ivery Hoover's affair and having another family. *(J. Edgar's family).*

Ivery's infidelity didn't stop him from having more children with his wife. The eighth child was Ruby, a girl, born in April 1899. She married George Austin. The nineth child was Bernard, born in 1903. The tenth child was Booker T., born in 1904. Number eleven was Mack, born in 1905. My mother knew him and talked about him a lot.

Clarence Allen was enumerated as a seven year old in the 1900 U.S. census of Pike county Mississippi. It was noted that the children had a limited amount of formal education. They worked the farm. My grandfather signed his draft registration card, and marriage license with a signature rather than an "X". Although he was illiterate.

According to the memory of the Oral history all sixteen children of Clarence and Litta were born and raised on the homestead property until a fire destroyed the property. After the fire, the home was rebuilt. Later there were tax problems, and the land was lost forever.

This work was the most freeing experience in my life. It gave me the lift that I needed to move forward, believing in myself, and wanting to give my best to others.

Big Daddy & Big Mama's Marriage Certificate
Listed as such; Clarence Allen & Litta Neal
Married: December 23, 1915.

Clarence Allen's Draft registration card
for the United States of America.

REGISTRATION CARD

1. Name in full Clarence Allen
   (Given name) (Family name)

2. Home address R.F.D.# Summit Miss
   (No.) (Street) (City) (State)

3. Date of birth April 9 1893
   (Month) (Day) (Year)

4. Are you (1) a natural-born citizen, (2) a naturalized citizen, (3) an alien, (4) or have you declared your intention (specify which)? natural-born

5. Where were you born? Lincoln Co. Miss U.S.A.
   (Town) (State) (Nation)

6. If not a citizen, of what country are you a citizen or subject?

7. What is your present trade, occupation, or office? Farming

8. By whom employed? self employ
   Where employed? R.F.D.# Summit

9. Have you a father, mother, wife, child under 12, or a sister or brother under 12, solely dependent on you for support (specify which)? wife + one child

10. Married or single (which)? Married Race (specify which)? African

11. What military service have you had? Rank _____ ; branch _____
    years _____ ; Nation or State _____

12. Do you claim exemption from draft (specify grounds)? none

I affirm that I have verified above answers and that they are true.

Clarence Allen
(Signature or mark)

- 22 -

Clarence Allen, was tall, thin, and handsome.
A young man, and a United States Citizen.

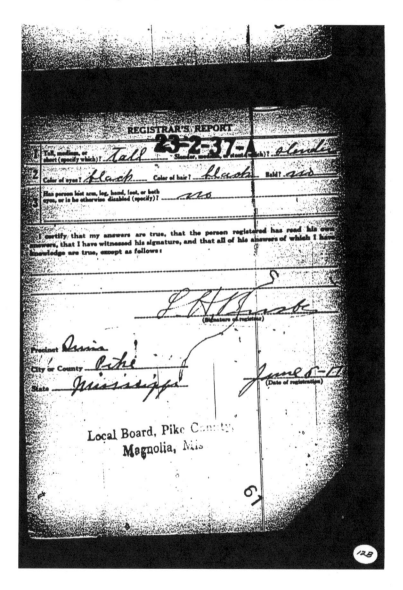

Happy to find Uncle Ebenezer Allen's Marriage records.
Mother talked about him a lot!

MARRIAGE BOND

THE STATE OF MISSISSIPPI, PIKE COUNTY.

KNOW ALL MEN BY THESE PRESENTS:

That we, _Ebenezer Allen_

and _Jeff Neal_

of the County of Pike, and State of Mississippi, are held and firmly bound unto the State of Mississippi, aforesaid, in the sum of One Hundred Dollars, lawful money of said State, to which payment well and truly to be made and performed, and we, and each of us. do bind ourselves, our heirs, executors, administrators and assigns, jointly, severally and firmly by these presents

Sealed with our seals, and dated this _24th_ day of _Sept_ Eighteen Hundred and _Eighty Eighth_

The Condition of this Obligation is such. That whereas a Marriage is shortly intended to be celebrated between the above bound _Ebenezer Allen_ and _Miss Ester Robinson_ Now, if there be no lawful cause to obstruct the said Marriage, then this obligation to be void, otherwise to remain in full force and virtue.

Signed, sealed and delivered in presence of

Ebenezer Allen (L. S.)
Jeff x Neal (L. S.)
(L. S.)

THE STATE OF MISSISSIPPI. PIKE COUNTY.

Before me, _A. P. Spurlman_ Clerk of the Circuit Court, in and for the County and State aforesaid, this day personally appeared _Ebenezer Allen & Jeff Neal_ and made oath that _Ebenezer Allen_ and _Miss Ester Robinson_ have arrived at the statutory age for the contraction of marriage, to-wit: 21 years and 18 years respectively, and further, that there exists no legal cause or objection to the marriage of the said _Ebenezer Allen_ and _Miss Ester Robinson_

Sworn to and subscribed before me, this _24_ day of _Sept_ 188

A. P. Spurkman Circuit Clerk.

Ebenezer x Allen
Jeff x Neal

THE STATE OF MISSISSIPPI. PIKE COUNTY.

To any Judge, Minister, Justice, or Other person Lawfully authorized to Celebrate the Rites of Matrimony:

You are Hereby Licensed to Celebrate the RITES OF MATRIMONY between Mr. _Ebenezer Allen_ and Miss _Ester Robinson_ and for so doing this shall be your warrant.

Given under my hand and official seal, this _24_ day of _Sept_ in the year of our Lord, One Thousand Eight Hundred and _Eighty Eight_

A. P. Spurkman Clerk

_1060_
_188__
_52_
_7/73_

THE STATE OF MISSISSIPPI, PIKE COUNTY.

In virtue of a License from the Clerk of the Circuit Court of said County of Pike, I have this day joined the RITES OF MATRIMONY between Mr. _Ebenezer Allen_ & _Ester Robinson_

Given under my hand and seal, this _1st_ day of _October_ A.D. 1888

Wm Harris M.G.

Recorded this _10_ day of _November_ 1888

- 24 -

The beginning:
Joseph Hoover, 1725 father of John Hoover 1747, who fathered Christian Hoover, 1847 who fathered Christian Hoover 1796, who fathered William Hoover, 1832. Who was Clarence Allen's grandfather.

etral File (TM) - ver 4.19   PEDIGREE CHART   18 NOV 1998   Chart _____

: on this chart is the same as no. _____ on chart no. _____

```
                                                                    16 Joseph HOOVER---------->
                                                                       AFN: 1MGH-M2J
                                              8 John HOOVER----------------- BORN: Abt 1725
                                                AFN: 1MGH-M4X
                                                BORN: Abt 1747              17 <Unknown>-------------
                                                South Carolina                AFN: 1MGH-HJQ
                                                MAR.:                         BORN: <1725>
                          4 Christian HOOVER----------------
Ancestral File Number       AFN: 1B6J-GRS               DIED: Abt 1802
                            BORN: Abt 1772              South Carolina
                            Of Orangeburg Di, , SC                          18 -----------------------
                            MAR.:                                              AFN:
                            South Carolina        9 Mary RUMPH-------------------- BORN:
                            DIED: Abt 1815          AFN: 1MGC-RQS
Christian HOOVER-----------------                   BORN: <1750>            19 -----------------------
AFN: 1MGC-8XG                                        <South Carolina>          AFN:
BORN: 24 Nov 1796                                   DIED:                       BORN:
Orangeburg District,S
MAR.: 8 Apr 1823                                                            20 -----------------------
Mississippi                                     10 -----------------------      AFN:
DIED: 17 Jul 1868                                  AFN:                         BORN:
Summit,P. Mississippi                              BORN:
                                                                           21 -----------------------
                                                   MAR.:                       AFN:
                          5 HOOK------------------------                        BORN:
                            AFN: 1MGC-8W8               DIED:
                            BORN: <1774>                                    22 -----------------------
                            <South Carolina>                                   AFN:
                            DIED:                                              BORN:
                                              11 -----------------------
William HOOVER-----------------                    AFN:                     23 -----------------------
AFN: 1MGC-6TH                                       BORN:                       AFN:
BORN: 25 Jan 1832                                                              BORN:
Oak Grove, Pike Co. Miss                           DIED:
MAR.: 27 Jul 1852                                                          24 -----------------------
B.                                                                             AFN:
DIED: 14 Jan 1903                             12 -----------------------      BORN:
Myrtle Place.P. Miss.                              AFN:
                                                   BORN:                    25 -----------------------
SPOUSE                                                                         AFN:
Martha Leticia Jane THOMPSON                       MAR.:                        BORN:
AFN: 1MGC-RDQ
BORN: 20 Nov 1834         6 William NEYLAND----------------
Amite Co. Miss             AFN: 1MGC-3LJ               DIED:
DIED: 18 Sep 1916          BORN: <1781>
Houston, TX                <Oak Grove,P, Miss>                             26 -----------------------
                           MAR.:                                              AFN:
                                              13 -----------------------      BORN:
                           DIED:                   AFN:
                                                   BORN:                    27 -----------------------
Mary NEYLAND--------------------                                               AFN:
AFN: 1MGH-KNW                                       DIED:                      BORN:
BORN: 30 Aug 1807
Mississippi                                                                28 -----------------------
DIED: 3 Feb 1858                              14 -----------------------      AFN:
Oak Grove, Pike Co, Miss                          AFN:                         BORN:
                                                   BORN:
                                                                          29 -----------------------
                                                   MAR.:                       AFN:
                          7 Nancy--------------------------                     BORN:
                            AFN: 1MGC-3MQ              DIED:
                            BORN: <1785>                                   30 -----------------------
                            <Mississippi>                                      AFN:
                            DIED:                                              BORN:
                                              15 -----------------------
                                                   AFN:                     31 -----------------------
                                                   BORN:                       AFN:
                                                                              BORN:
                                                   DIED:
```

8A

Husband	CHRISTIAN HOOVER-26		See "Other Marriages"
Born	24 Nov 1796	Place ORANGEBURG DIST., SOUTH CAROLINA	
Christened		Place	
Died	17 Jul 1868	Place SUMMIT, PIKE, MISSISSIPPI	
Buried		Place	
Married	8 Apr 1823	Place MISSISSIPPI	
Husband's father	CHRISTIAN HOOVER-39		MRIN: 15 ☐ Deceased
Husband's mother	HOOK-40		☐ Deceased

Wife	MARY NEYLAND-38		See "Other Marriages"
Born	30 Aug 1807	Place MISSISSIPPI	
Christened		Place	
Died		Place	
Buried		Place	
Wife's father Given name(s)		Last name	☐ Deceased
Wife's mother Given name(s)		Maiden name	☐ Deceased

Children List each child in order of birth.

1	Sex M	WILLIAM HOOVER SLAVE OWNER-25		See "Other Marriages"
	Born	25 Jan 1832	Place PIKE CO., MISSISSIPPI	
	Christened		Place	
	Died	14 Jan 1903	Place MYRTLE PLACE, PIKE, MISSISSIPPI	
	Buried		Place	
	Spouse	EMILY ALLEN-6		MRIN: 2
	Married		Place	

Family Group Record - 2

Page 1 of 2

Husband	WILLIAM HOOVER SLAVE OWNER-25		See "Other Marriages"
Born	25 Jan 1832	Place PIKE CO., MISSISSIPPI	
Christened		Place	
Died	14 Jan 1903	Place MYRTLE PLACE, PIKE, MISSISSIPPI	
Buried		Place	
Married		Place	
Husband's father	CHRISTIAN HOOVER-26		MRIN: 6 · Deceased
Husband's mother	MARY NEYLAND-38		· Deceased

Wife	EMILY ALLEN-6		See "Other Marriages"
Born	Abt 1840	Place MISSISSIPPI	
Christened		Place	
Died		Place	
Buried		Place	
Wife's father Given name(s)		Last name	MRIN: 4 · Deceased
Wife's mother	EMILY OR EMILY ELIZABETH ALLEN-15		£ Deceased

Children List each child in order of birth.

	Sex			See "Other Marriages"
1	F	MALINDA ALLEN-12		
	Born	Jun 1860	Place MISSISSIPPI	
	Christened		Place	
	Died		Place	
	Buried		Place	
	Spouse	DAVID MANNING-14		MRIN: 3
	Married	Abt 1891	Place PROB. PIKE CO., MISSISSIPPI	
2	M	IVY HOOVER-11		See "Other Marriages"
	Born	May 1861	Place MISSISSIPPI	
	Christened		Place	
	Died		Place	
	Buried		Place	
	Spouse	ARIE -16		MRIN: 5
	Married		Place	
3	M	SIMON ALLEN-7		See "Other Marriages"
	Born	Abt 1862	Place MISSISSIPPI	
	Christened		Place	
	Died		Place	
	Buried		Place	
	Spouse			
	Married		Place	

- 27 -

Family Group Record - 2

Husband WILLIAM HOOVER SLAVE OWNER-25

Wife EMILY ALLEN-6

Children List each child in order of birth.

4 Sex M EBENEZER ALLEN-8
Born Abt 1864 — Place MISSISSIPPI
Christened — Place
Died — Place
Buried — Place
Spouse ESTHER ROBINSON-29 — MRIN: 9
Married 1 Oct 1888 — Place PIKE CO., MISSISSIPPI

5 Sex M WILLIAM ALLEN-2
Born Feb 1870 — Place PROB. PIKE CO., MISSISSIPPI
Christened — Place
Died — Place
Buried — Place
Spouse ELIZABETH HAYNES-3 — MRIN: 1
Married 27 Dec 1892 — Place PIKE CO., MISSISSIPPI

6 Sex F LIZZIE ALLEN-13
Born Abt 1868 — Place MISSISSIPPI
Christened — Place
Died — Place
Buried — Place
Spouse
Married — Place

7 Sex M HARRISON ALLEN-9
Born Abt 1872 — Place MISSISSIPPI
Christened — Place
Died — Place
Buried — Place
Spouse
Married — Place

8 Sex M WALTER ALLEN-10
Born Abt 1875 — Place MISSISSIPPI
Christened — Place
Died — Place
Buried — Place
Spouse
Married — Place

Family Group Record - 5

Husband	IVY HOOVER-11			See "Other Marriages" ☐
Born	May 1861	Place MISSISSIPPI		
Christened		Place		
Died		Place		
Buried		Place		
Married		Place		
Husband's father	WILLIAM HOOVER SLAVE OWNER-25		MRIN: 2	X Deceased
Husband's mother	EMILY ALLEN-6			☐ Deceased

Wife	ARIE -16			See "Other Marriages" X
Born		Place		
Christened		Place		
Died		Place		
Buried		Place		
Wife's father Given name(s)		Last name		☐ Deceased
Wife's mother Given name(s)		Maiden name		☐ Deceased

Children List each child in order of birth.

1	Sex M	EARNEST J HOOVER-17		See "Other Marriages" ☐
	Born	Aug 1881	Place PROB. PIKE CO., MISSISSIPPI	
	Christened		Place	
	Died		Place	
	Buried		Place	
	Spouse			
	Married		Place	

2	Sex M	EUGENE E. HOOVER-18		See "Other Marriages" ☐
	Born	Feb 1883	Place PROB. PIKE CO., MISSISSIPPI	
	Christened		Place	
	Died		Place	
	Buried		Place	
	Spouse			
	Married		Place	

3	Sex M	CHUNCY HOOVER-19		See "Other Marriages" ☐
	Born	Feb 1885	Place PROB. PIKE CO., MISSISSIPPI	
	Christened		Place	
	Died		Place	
	Buried		Place	
	Spouse	HATTIE COCKERHAM-30		MRIN: 10
	Married	23 Feb 1913	Place PIKE CO., MISSISSIPPI	

Husband IVY HOOVER-11

Wife ARIE -16

Children List each child in order of birth.

4. **Sex** M **MARCINA HOOVER-20** *See "Other Marriages"*

Born	Oct 1886	Place PROB. PIKE CO., MISSISSIPPI
Christened		Place
Died		Place
Buried		Place
Spouse	MATTIE COCKRAM-32	MRIN: 12
Married	11 Feb 1910	Place PIKE CO., MISSISSIPPI

5. **Sex** M **CHRIS HOOVER-21** *See "Other Marriages"*

Born	Jun 1887	Place PROB. PIKE CO., MISSISSIPPI
Christened		Place
Died		Place
Buried		Place
Spouse		
Married		Place

6. **Sex** M **CLEMENTINE HOOVER-22** *See "Other Marriages"*

Born	Dec 1892	Place PROB. PIKE CO., MISSISSIPPI
Christened		Place
Died		Place
Buried		Place
Spouse	SILAS HARRIS-31	MRIN: 11
Married	23 Jul 1911	Place PIKE CO., MISSISSIPPI

7. **Sex** F **MOZILLA HOOVER-23** *See "Other Marriages"*

Born	May 1896	Place PROB PIKE CO., MISSISSIPPI
Christened		Place
Died		Place
Buried		Place
Spouse		
Married		Place

8. **Sex** F **RUBY HOOVER-24** *See "Other Marriages"*

Born	Apr 1899	Place PROB. PIKE CO., MISSISSIPPI
Christened		Place
Died		Place
Buried		Place
Spouse	GEORGE AUSTIN-33	MRIN: 13
Married	18 Apr 1915	Place PIKE CO., MISSISSIPPI

9. **Sex** M **BERNARD HOOVER-35** *See "Other Marriages"*

Born	Abt 1903	Place PROB. PIKE CO., MISSISSIPPI
Christened		Place
Died		Place
Buried		Place
Spouse		
Married		Place

18 Mar 1999

Husband	IVY HOOVER-11
Wife	ARIE -16

Children List each child in order of birth.

10 **Sex M** **BOOKER T. HOOVER-36** — See "Other Marriages"

Born	Abt 1904	Place PROB PIKE CO.. MISSISSIPPI
Christened		Place
Died		Place
Buried		Place
Spouse		
Married		Place

11 **Sex M** **MACK HOOVER-37** — See "Other Marriages"

Born	Abt 1905	Place PROB. PIKE CO.. MISSISSIPPI
Christened		Place
Died		Place
Buried		Place
Spouse		
Married		Place

Other marriages

WIFE - ARIE -16
25 Dec 1918   SYLVESTER BULLOCK-34   MRIN: 14

Christian Hoover 1796-1868
State Senator, Judge, and Minister.
He was Clarence Allen's great grandfather.

Pedigree Chart

8 CHRISTIAN HOOVER-26
B: 24 Nov 1796
P :'OD,SOUTH CAROLINA
M: 8 Apr 1823 - 6
P : MISSISSIPPI
D: 17 Jul 1868
P : SUMMIT,PIKE,MISSISSIPPI

4 WILLIAM HOOVER SLAVE OWNER-25
B: 25 Jan 1832
P : PIKE CO .,MISSISSIPPI
M: ~ 2
P :
D: 14 Jan 1903
P : MYRTLE PLACE,PIKE,MISSISSIPPI

9 MARY NEYLAND-38
B: 30 Aug 1807
P : MISSISSIPPI
D:
P :

2 WILLIAM ALLEN-2
B: Feb 1870
P : PROB. PIKE CO.,MISSISSIPPI
M: 27 Dec 1892 - 1
P : PIKE CO.,MISSISSIPPI
D:
P :

10
B:
P:
M:
P:
B: ~ 4
P:

5 EMILY ALLEN-6
B: Abt 1840
P : MISSISSIPPI
D:
P :

11 EMILY OR EMILY ELIZABETH ALLEN-15
B: Abt 1814
P : MARYLAND
D: Aft 1870
P : PROB. PIKE CO.,MISSISSIPPI

1 CLARENCE ALLEN-1
B: 9 Apr 1893
P : LINCOLN CO.,MISSISSIPPI
M: 26 Dec 1915 - 7
P : PIKE CO.,MISSISSIPPI
D: Aug 1967
P : PIKE CO .,MISSISSIPPI

12
B:
P:
M:
P:
D:
P:

6
B:
P:
M:
P:
D:
P:

LETTA NEAL-27
(Spouse of no. 1)

13
B:
P:
D:
P:

3 ELIZABETH HAYNES-3
B: Nov 1870
P : MISSISSIPPI
D:
P :

14
B:
P:
M:
P:
D:
P:

7
B:
P:
D:
P:

15
B:
P:
D:
P:

Husband WILLIAM ALLEN-2   See "Other Marriages"

Born	Feb 1870	Place PROB. PIKE CO., MISSISSIPPI
Christened		Place
Died		Place
Buried		Place
Married	27 Dec 1892	Place PIKE CO., MISSISSIPPI

Husband's father WILLIAM HOOVER SLAVE OWNER-25   MRIN: 2   X Deceased

Husband's mother EMILY ALLEN-6   ☐ Deceased

Wife ELIZABETH HAYNES-3   See "Other Marriages"

Born	Nov 1870	Place MISSISSIPPI
Christened		Place
Died		Place
Buried		Place

Wife's father Given name(s)   Last name   ☐ Deceased

Wife's mother Given name(s)   Maiden name   ☐ Deceased

Children List each child in order of birth.

1 Sex M CLARENCE ALLEN-1   See "Other Marriages"

Born	9 Apr 1893	Place LINCOLN CO., MISSISSIPPI
Christened		Place
Died		Place
Buried	Aug 1967	Place PIKE CO., MISSISSIPPI
Spouse	LETTA NEAL-27	MRIN: 7
Married	26 Dec 1915	Place PIKE CO., MISSISSIPPI

2 Sex F FLORENCE ALLEN-4   See "Other Marriages"

Born	Nov 1894	Place PROB. PIKE CO., MISSISSIPPI
Christened		Place
Died		Place
Buried		Place
Spouse	MACON WASHINGTON-28	MRIN: 8
Married	2 Mar 1914	Place PIKE CO., MISSISSIPPI

3 Sex F ROSA A. ALLEN-5   See "Other Marriages"

Born	Dec 1896	Place PROB. PIKE CO., MISSISSIPPI
Christened		Place
Died		Place
Buried		Place
Spouse		
Married		Place

18 Mar 1999

Husband	CLARENCE ALLEN-1		See "Other Marriages"
Born	9 Apr 1893	Place LINCOLN CO., MISSISSIPPI	
Christened		Place	
Died	Aug 1967	Place PIKE CO., MISSISSIPPI	
Buried		Place	
Married	26 Dec 1915	Place PIKE CO., MISSISSIPPI	
Husband's father	WILLIAM ALLEN-2	MRIN: 1	☐ Deceased
Husband's mother	ELIZABETH HAYNES-3		☐ Deceased

Wife	LETTA NEAL-27		See "Other Marriages"
Born		Place	
Christened		Place	
Died		Place	
Buried		Place	
Wife's father Given name(s)		Last name	☐ Deceased
Wife's mother Given name(s)		Maiden name	☐ Deceased

Children List each child in order of birth.

	Sex Given name(s)		Last name	See "Other Marriages"
1	Born (day month year)	Place		
	Christened	Place		
	Died	Place		
	Spouse Given name(s)		Last name	
	Married	Place		

Washington DC Hoovers.
J. Edgar Hoover's Claimed Relative.
William Hoover, and Elizabeth A.

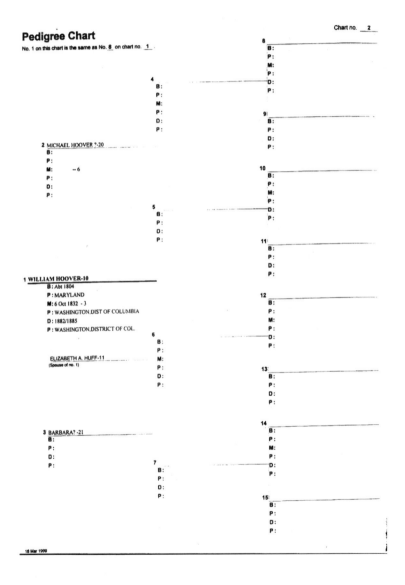

Pedigree Chart

Chart no. ___2___

No. 1 on this chart is the same as No. 8 on chart no. 1 .

8
B:
P:
M:
P:
D:
P:

4
B:
P:
M:
P:
D:
P:

9
B:
P:
D:
P:

2 MICHAEL HOOVER ?-20
B:
P:
M: — 6
P:
D:
P:

10
B:
P:
M:
P:
D:
P:

5
B:
P:
D:
P:

11
B:
P:
D:
P:

1 WILLIAM HOOVER-10
B: Abt 1804
P: MARYLAND
M: 6 Oct 1832 - 3
P: WASHINGTON,DIST OF COLUMBIA
D: 1882/1885
P: WASHINGTON,DISTRICT OF COL.

12
B:
P:
M:
P:
D:
P:

6
B:
P:
M:
P:
D:
P:

ELIZABETH A. HUFF-11
(Spouse of no. 1)

13
B:
P:
D:
P:

14
B:
P:
M:
P:
D:
P:

3 BARBARA? -21
B:
P:
D:
P:

7
B:
P:
D:
P:

15
B:
P:
D:
P:

16 Mar 1999

Family Group Record - 6

Husband MICHAEL HOOVER ?-20 — See "Other Marriages"

Born	Place
Christened	Place
Died	Place
Buried	Place
Married	Place

Husband's father Given name(s)	Last name	☐ Deceased
Husband's mother Given name(s)	Maiden name	☐ Deceased

Wife BARBARA? -21 — See "Other Marriages"

Born	Place
Christened	Place
Died	Place
Buried	Place

Wife's father Given name(s)	Last name	☐ Deceased
Wife's mother Given name(s)	Maiden name	☐ Deceased

Children List each child in order of birth.

1 M JOHN HOOVER-22 — See "Other Marriages"

Born	1790/1800 Place
Christened	Place
Died	Place
Buried	Place
Spouse	
Married	Place

2 M MICHAEL HOOVER-23 — See "Other Marriages"

Born	1790/1800 Place
Christened	Place
Died	Place
Buried	Place
Spouse	
Married	Place

3 M WILLIAM HOOVER-10 — See "Other Marriages"

Born	Abt 1804 Place MARYLAND
Christened	Place
Died	1882/1885 Place WASHINGTON, DISTRICT OF COL.
Buried	Place
Spouse	ELIZABETH A. HUFF-11 — MRIN: 3
Married	6 Oct 1832 Place WASHINGTON, DIST OF COLUMBIA

Husband	WILLIAM HOOVER-10
Wife	ELIZABETH A. HUFF-11

Children List each child in order of birth.

4 Sex M **MILTON HOOVER-14**

See "Other Marriages"

Born	Abt 1845	Place WASHINGTON, DIST OF COLUMBIA
Christened		Place
Died		Place
Buried		Place
Spouse		
Married		Place

5 Sex M **CLAYTON A. HOOVER-15**

See "Other Marriages"

Born	Abt 1853	Place WASHINGTON, DIST OF COLUMBIA
Christened		Place
Died		Place
Buried		Place
Spouse		
Married		Place

6 Sex M **WILLIAM E. HOOVER-16**

See "Other Marriages"

Born	Abt 1855	Place WASHINTON, DIST OF COLUMBIA
Christened		Place
Died		Place
Buried		Place
Spouse		
Married		Place

7 Sex F **LULA A. HOOVER-17**

See "Other Marriages"

Born	Abt 1857	Place WASHINGTON, DIST OF COLUMBIA
Christened		Place
Died		Place
Buried		Place
Spouse		
Married		Place

18 Mar 1999

J. Edgar Hoover's Claimed Family!
Allen Family's Oral History states he was Ivery Hoover's outside child.

Pedigree Chart

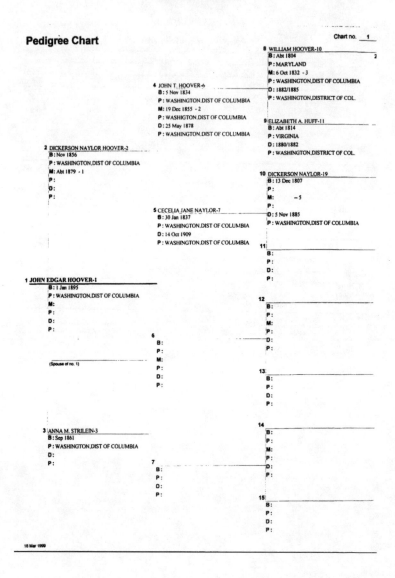

8 WILLIAM HOOVER-10
B: Abt 1804   2
P: MARYLAND
M: 6 Oct 1832 - 3
P: WASHINGTON,DIST OF COLUMBIA
D: 1882/1885
P: WASHINGTON,DISTRICT OF COL.

4 JOHN T. HOOVER-6
B: 5 Nov 1834
P: WASHINGTON,DIST OF COLUMBIA
M: 19 Dec 1855 - 2
P: WASHIGTON,DIST OF COLUMBIA
D: 25 May 1878
P: WASHINGTON,DIST OF COLUMBIA

9 ELIZABETH A. HUFF-11
B: Abt 1814
P: VIRGINIA
D: 1880/1882
P: WASHINGTON,DISTRICT OF COL.

2 DICKERSON NAYLOR HOOVER-2
B: Nov 1856
P: WASHINGTON,DIST OF COLUMBIA
M: Abt 1879 - 1
P:
D:
P:

10 DICKERSON NAYLOR-19
B: 13 Dec 1807
P:
M: - 5
P:
D: 5 Nov 1885
P: WASHINGTON,DIST OF COLUMBIA

5 CECELIA JANE NAYLOR-7
B: 30 Jan 1837
P: WASHINGTON,DIST OF COLUMBIA
D: 14 Oct 1909
P: WASHINGTON,DIST OF COLUMBIA

11
B:
P:
D:
P:

1 JOHN EDGAR HOOVER-1
B: 1 Jan 1895
P: WASHINGTON,DIST OF COLUMBIA
M:
P:
D:
P:

12
B:
P:
M:
P:
D:
P:

6
B:
P:
M:
P:
D:
P:

(Spouse of no. 1)

13
B:
P:
D:
P:

3 ANNA M. STRILEIN-3
B: Sep 1861
P: WASHINGTON,DIST OF COLUMBIA
D:
P:

14
B:
P:
M:
P:
D:
P:

7
B:
P:
D:
P:

15
B:
P:
D:
P:

18 Mar 1999

Husband	JOHN T. HOOVER-6		See "Other Marriages"
Born	5 Nov 1834	Place WASHINGTON. DIST OF COLUMBIA	
Christened		Place	
Died	25 May 1878	Place WASHINGTON. DIST OF COLUMBIA	
Buried		Place ROCK CREEK CEM.. WASHINTON. DIST OF COLUMBIA	
Married	19 Dec 1855	Place WASHIGTON. DIST OF COLUMBIA	
Husband's father	WILLIAM HOOVER-10	MRIN: 3	⊠ Deceased
Husband's mother	ELIZABETH A. HUFF-11		X Deceased

Wife	CECELIA JANE NAYLOR-7		See "Other Marriages"
Born	30 Jan 1837	Place WASHINGTON. DIST OF COLUMBIA	
Christened		Place	
Died	14 Oct 1909	Place WASHINGTON. DIST OF COLUMBIA	
Buried		Place ROCK CREEK CEM. WASHINGTON. DIST OF COLUMBIA	
Wife's father	DICKERSON NAYLOR-19	MRIN: 5	⊠ Deceased
Wife's mother Given name(s)		Maiden name	☐ Deceased

Children List each child in order of birth.

1	Sex M	DICKERSON NAYLOR HOOVER-2		See "Other Marriages"
	Born	Nov 1856	Place WASHINGTON, DIST OF COLUMBIA	
	Christened		Place	
	Died		Place	
	Buried		Place	
	Spouse	ANNA M. STRILEIN-3	MRIN: 1	
	Married	Abt 1879	Place	

2	Sex M	WILLIAM B. HOOVER-8		See "Other Marriages"
	Born	Abt 1863	Place WASHINGTON, DIST OF COLUMBIA	
	Christened		Place	
	Died		Place	
	Buried		Place	
	Spouse			
	Married		Place	

3	Sex M	HALSTED P. HOOVER-9		See "Other Marriages"
	Born	May 1870	Place WASHINGTON, DIST OF COLUMBIA	
	Christened		Place	
	Died		Place	
	Buried		Place	
	Spouse			
	Married		Place	

18 Mar 1999

Family Group Record - 1

Husband   DICKERSON NAYLOR HOOVER-2

See "Other Marriages"

Born	Nov 1856	Place WASHINGTON, DIST OF COLUMBIA
Christened		Place
Died		Place
Buried		Place
Married	Abt 1879	Place

Husband's father   JOHN T. HOOVER-6   MRIN: 2   X Deceased

Husband's mother   CECELIA JANE NAYLOR-7   X Deceased

Wife   ANNA M. STRILEIN-3

See "Other Marriages"

Born	Sep 1861	Place WASHINGTON, DIST OF COLUMBIA
Christened		Place
Died		Place
Buried		Place

Wife's father
Given name(s)   Last name   Deceased

Wife's mother
Given name(s)   Maiden name   Deceased

Children   List each child in order of birth.

1   Sex M   DICKERSON NAYLOR HOOVER-4

See "Other Marriages"

Born	Sep 1880	Place WASHINGTON, DIST OF COLUMBIA
Christened		Place
Died		Place
Buried		Place
Spouse	THEODORA -18	
Married		Place

MRIN: 4

2   Sex F   LILLIAN HOOVER-5

See "Other Marriages"

Born	Nov 1882	Place WASHINGTON, DIST OF COLUMBIA
Christened		Place
Died		Place
Buried		Place
Spouse		
Married		Place

3   Sex M   JOHN EDGAR HOOVER-1

See "Other Marriages"

Born	1 Jan 1895	Place WASHINGTON, DIST OF COLUMBIA
Christened		Place
Died		Place
Buried		Place
Spouse		
Married		Place

18 Mar 1999

- 40 -

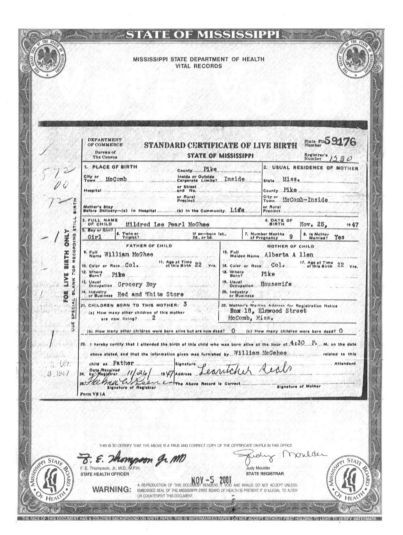

DEPARTMENT OF COMMERCE
Bureau of The Census

STANDARD CERTIFICATE OF LIVE BIRTH
STATE OF MISSISSIPPI

State File Number 59176
Registrar's Number 1230

1. PLACE OF BIRTH
County Pike

City or Town McComb
Inside or Outside Corporate Limits? Inside

Hospital

Mother's Stay Before Delivery—(a) In Hospital (b) In the Community Life

2. USUAL RESIDENCE OF MOTHER
State Miss.
County Pike
City or Town McComb-Inside
or Rural Precinct

3. FULL NAME OF CHILD Mildred Lee Pearl McGhee

4. DATE OF BIRTH Nov. 25, 1947

5. Boy or Girl? Girl
6. Twin or Triplet?
If so—born 1st., 2d., or 3d.
7. Number Months of Pregnancy 9
8. Is Mother Married? Yes

FATHER OF CHILD

9. Full Name William McGhee
10. Color or Race Col.
11. Age at Time of this Birth 22 Yrs.
12. Where Born? Pike
13. Usual Occupation Grocery Boy
14. Industry or Business Red and White Store

MOTHER OF CHILD

15. Full Maiden Name Alberta Allen
16. Color or Race Col.
17. Age at Time of this Birth 22 Yrs.
18. Where Born? Pike
19. Usual Occupation Housewife
20. Industry or Business

21. CHILDREN BORN TO THIS MOTHER: 3
(a) How many other children of this mother are now living? 2

22. Mother's Mailing Address for Registration Notice
Box 18, Elmwood Street
McComb, Miss.

(b) How many other children were born alive but are now dead? O
(c) How many children were born dead? O

23. I hereby certify that I attended the birth of this child who was born alive at the hour of 4:30 P. M. on the date above stated, and that the information given was furnished by William McGhee related to this child as Father Signature Attendant

24. Date Received by Registrar 11/26/1947 Address Leantcher Seals

Signature of Registrar The Above Record is Correct Signature of Mother

Form VS 1A

Author's birth record.

Author visits the Grave Site in McComb, giving special time, and love to her grandparents. Clarence & Lydia Allen.

Here lies my sister "Re Re" Eddis Marie McGhee.

My Hero, Big Daddy.

Big Daddy's 1st Son, Willie Tyre "Jack Allen" 1918-1974.

Mississippi Trip to review research with J.E. Hoover's claimed relatives...
April 2002

The Bogue Chitto Grave Site.

The Hoover Plantation Grave Site located on the Plantation History revealed April 2000. We found Ivery Hoover.

Ivery Hoover (1859 - 1917)
"The Mystery Man"
Laid to rest on the Plantation near his father, Judge, Senator,
and Minister of Mississippi.
Christian "Kit" Hoover (1796 - 1868)

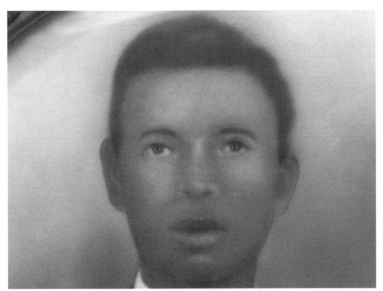

Granddad - William Allen,
1870-1937
who should have carried the
surname Hoover.

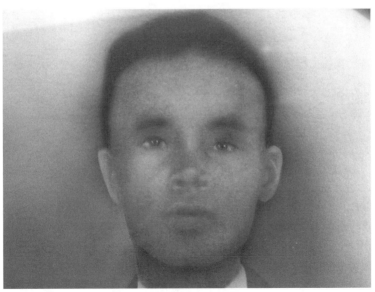

Clarence Allen, "Big Daddy."
1893-1967

Artwork by LaTasha Tobias

Two Families
The Allen's and Hoover's

WHAT CENSUS RECORDS LOOKS LIKE:

Above is a 1900 census that shows William and Elizabeth A. Hoover's grandson, Dickerson Hoover, with his wife, Anna M., his son Dickerson Jr., age 19, his daughter Lillian, age 17, and a small boy John E., age 5.

"White, Black, or Mulatto, " usually the census taker puts W, B, or M. I'm not sure those are reliable. This shows William Allen as black, and changed to white. Those kinds of mistakes were uncommon in the National Archives. They would take notes and rewrite it clearly to ensure accurate family records. Many f errors were found in my family files, so that they could pass for white.

This is uncommon to see in the National Archives...
This looks like an erased or tampered record, found in the census where my family's records should be found connecting the Allens and the Hoovers. "He will erase his records." Big Daddy said. This validates the Oral History.

View of another census record, showing head of household, William Hoover, wife Elizabeth A., and then listing children. It It's believed that this is Elizabeth Allen, Emily Allen's mother.

The Author's Views
On The Research

Crossing The Color Line

When researching someone's ancestry, think about how records were affected by the pressures African Americans faced in the 1800s and early 1900s. It had to be tempting for people of color with very light skin to think about passing as white.

During slavery, freed black people could be jailed, or even sold, if they could not prove they were free. Our research shows a good example of that. A freed black man, named Henry Brown, was held in jail and only after John Hoover vouched for him did they set him free.

Before and after slavery, even a drop of colored blood could mean that you would be denied career appointments. It was impossible to gain a high position in government for dark skinned black people, still even in the early 1960's.

Seeing these dangers, if we knew that our child had an opportunity to pass for white, who knows what any of us would have done? I would have passed, so that I could help my people. I believe a lot of us did pass, and are in high places today helping many of us move forward.

When researching my ancestors in the archives, and looking at J. Edgar Hoover's ancestry, I found that the records did not handle this well. They tried to classify people as "W" for (white), "B" for (black), and "M" for (mulatto). However, they often didn't get it right. The same person who shows in one census as black sometimes shows up in another as mulatto, and on his military papers they classify him as white.

In one of the few statistical studies done on this topic, researchers in sociology and anthropology show that as many as 155,500 people passed from the Negro group to the White group between 1940 and 1950.

That means that in the century of J. Edgar Hoover's lifetime, and while his parents were growing up, nearly a million people crossed the color line. So you see, about one million census records are incorrect. The first thing a genealogist does when he wants to prove whether a person has African American ancestry is go to documents like census enumerations and military records. Those records assign a race to each person.

If one million people were running around giving out incorrect racial information, should we really take written documents in favor of oral family history? I don't think so. Especially when the grandchildren are still alive.

Many genealogists tend to discount the powerful tradition of oral history among African Americans. Our tradition goes all the way back to Africa, where a designated person was required to memorize the family history for an entire tribe. These histories became so complicated that we started memorizing information and passing it on to each generation. It's sad to say that I've noticed young people today are not as interested in the oral tradition. It's due to lack of sharing our life stories to the young people today.

For slave families, oral stories of our history were the only way they could hold on to a sense of family. Slaves were often separated, and most were not taught to read. Our oral family history tradition comes from our ancestors passed down through generations, which is a thousand-year-old cultural tradition.

How Did People Pass?

Most people didn't know that hundreds of thousands of people changed their racial identity in the1800's. When they did, they didn't just stay in the same house with the same family, in the same neighborhood, and keep the same name. To me, common sense would tell you that they moved, changed their names, and misled a few people on their vital statistics. They would have had to, in order to protect themselves!

"The Other Underground Railroad"

Most people think of the Underground Railroad as a system to guide African Americans to freedom. Everyone thought that both white people and black people helped, but we don't have any documents proving that. What if this was something that the African Americans cooked up to free themselves, using the light skinned, blue eyes mulatto blacks to help find freedom. Most of us in the African American community know of relatives who have chosen to pass, and we have heard about some of the things they had to do.

The "fantasy" portion of this book shows how people protected each other and misled record-keepers.

We haven't heard much about the "other" Underground Railroad, "Passing for White." One reason I wrote this book was to show that not all the relationships between whites and blacks were abusive during slavery.

Just as whites and blacks offered assistance to blacks trying to escape slavery, they sympathetically helped light-skinned African Americans who were in the process of crossing the color barrier, so our history says.

Doctoring the Documents

One of the strangest records is J. Edgar Hoover's birth record. Each birth record has the same information, except J. Edgar's. Each one has a number and the numbers are pretty much in order, except J. Edgar's. His record was obviously added some years later, after the fact.

<u>**Here is what the birth records look like:**</u>

Hooks, William & Annie	67834
Hoover, Clayton & Julia	72632
Hooke, Franci J & Maggie	88300
Hoover, William H & Mary A	88688

Tacked on at the end, in a different pen:

Hoover, Dickerson N. & Annie M.	41902

John Edgar 1-1-95 m -w (male - white)
(ACTUAL DOCUMENT ON NEXT PAGE.)

This is how records were kept back in the 1800's.
J. Edgar Hoover's doctored birth records.

Who Was J. Edgar Hoover's Mother?

When J. Edgar was five years old, Anna (Annie) M. Hoover was listed as his mother starting in the 1900 D.C. census. To view the census records, (see page 49.) Dickerson Hoover was her husband, and they had three children.

In the 1910 D.C. census, Anna Hoover is missing. She showed up in Pike County, MS in the 1910 census with Ivery Hoover. We believe this was during the time her husband was hospitalized. Ivery was separated from his wife, and we found records that she remarried after his death.

Now this validates the Allen Oral History that Ivery was her lover, and fathered J. Edgar. By 1920, the census showed her listed in the D.C. census, grouped with Dickerson N. Hoover as head of household. Dickerson was released in **1917** from the sanitarium, the same year Ivery Hoover died.

It was hard to find documents on Anna M. Hoover's ancestry. She was mulatto. We found two photos of her. I looked at her photos carefully. One of the photos we found was J. Edgar Hoover's mother shown with Dickerson, and a child. The second photo is the mother he had while he was in power as the director of the FBI. (*This could be his housekeeper.*)

Note features between J. Edgar & Mom #1

Mom #1

She has a round race, flat cheekbones, pointed nose, much like J. Edgar's, and her upper lip shows a wide space between her mouth and nose.

Mom #2

She had high cheekbones, a triangular face, flat pointed nose, and a narrow space between mouth and nose.

When I read the book, *"J. Edgar Hoover: The Man and The Secrets,"* by Curt Gentry, I noticed the photo of his mother as a young woman. Then later in the book as an older woman, it appeared strange that they looked different to me.

This same picture below shows the younger mother with J. Edgar, but it is not "Edgar, " or "J. E.," with his parents. It's his brother Dickerson. (see below)

I have also found in my research a Certificate of Birth signed by John Edgar Hoover, which was filed Sept. 21, 1938. There was a statement given before a notary at the time of the filing for his birth records, by his brother Dickerson. Dickerson appears in the photo above, giving J. E. his identity when J. E. wasn't born yet. That is indeed Dickerson at five years old with his father, Dickerson Naylor Hoover Sr., and his mother, Annie Scheitlin Hoover. *(statement below)*

State of Maryland, County of Prince George. I, Dickerson N. Hoover, of Glenn Dale, Maryland, son of Dickerson N. Hoover, and Annie S. Hoover, depose and say that I was present at the birth of and know of my own knowledge that my brother, John Edgar Hoover, was born in the home of our parents, 413 Seward Square, Southeast, Washington, D.C., on January 1, 1895. At the time of John Edgar Hoover's birth I was 15 years of age. SEAL

Note the resemblance between the two young boys, "Who or Which one is "J.E?"

It appears that the rumor about this five year old boy here being Dickerson Jr, not J.E, is true! We found evidence stating that this boy is not J.E, but is Dickerson Jr!

This picture of this boy at age four is J. Edgar Hoover.

These pictures are from National Archives. "Rumor has it" the picture of the five year old is actually Dickerson Jr, J. Edgar's half brother. He gave a statement to help J. Edgar get a real birth certificate. Dickerson and his family were disinherited in J. Edgar's will.

What About J. Edgar's Brother And Sister?

J. Edgar was said to have one brother, Dickerson Naylor Hoover Jr., and one sister, Lillian Hoover. In a time when birth control pills didn't exist, J. Edgar was born more than a decade after his siblings. His brother was 14 years older, and his sister was 12 years older than he. But yet he stated that he was 15 years old at the time of J.E's birth. By 1917, his sister Lillian was ill. Dickerson Jr. and J. Edgar became the family's sole supporters.

What About J. Edgar?

He was born January 1, 1895. Who were his parents? We found many clues that showed who his real father was. The clues were important, concerning the rumors about J. Edgar being Ivery Hoover's outside child. The truth is this:

Clue #1. We found this clue in the Gentry biography on page 116. It states, "Considering the meteoric rise, Hoover should have been happy. There are reasons to believe he wasn't. **The same year Hoover was appointed BI Chief, his father died.**" *(What year did his father die?)*

Clue # 2. We found out that J. Edgar was appointed BI Chief in **1917.** Answer to the question, when did his father die? **1917***!*

Clue #3. In the genealogy research on the Allens and the Hoovers, we found Ivery Hoover's gravesite on the Hoover plantation. He died *November 18, 1917.* (See page 222.)

J. Edgar's relationship with father, Dickerson N. Hoover, was virtually non-existent. According to his friends, he never discussed his father. Dickerson Hoover didn't die until **1921**. J. Edgar's biological father was Ivery Hoover.

Clue #4. On page 68 of Gentry's book, "In 1913 while Hoover was still a senior at Central High, Dickerson was placed in a sanitarium near Laurel, Maryland, for what was termed a nervous breakdown.

Although released after several months, his condition - which was characterized by alternating moods of irritability and inconsolable sadness - worsened and on April 5, 1917, the day before war was declared, he was forced to resign his $2000 a year job with the U.S.Coast and Geodetic Survey." So, Dickerson N. Hoover was still alive in 1917!

What father died in 1917? Continuing...

J. Edgar Hoover obtained frightening power at an amazingly young age, just two years after graduating from college. His rise was rapid. That Justice Department was understaffed. Many of its young men having enlisted, was only one part of the reason. His superiors were impressed. So impressed that less than three months after his arrival, in **1917**, he was promoted. And then three months later, promoted again.

At the age of 22, John Edgar Hoover had found his niche in life. He had become a hunter of men.

We found in Curt Gentry's book, this clear documentation, "In February 1919 Attorney General Thomas Gregory submitted his resignation. The next to leave was A. Bruce Fielaski, who was replaced as Chief of the Bureau of Investigation by William E. Allen."

(Who was this William E. Allen?)

"**William Allen** served as chief of the Bureau of Investigation for so short a time, less than six months, that he is lost in the cracks of most Bureau histories." The Allen Oral History stated, a family member appointed J. Edgar Hoover to the Bureau. The author's great grandfather and uncle was named William Allen. He was the son of William Hoover.

(Could this be a cousin?)

One of J. Edgar's first assignments in *1917*, was collecting secret files on Americans. By the time he was 27, he was the director of the Bureau of Investigation, which is now called the FBI. He held on to that position for nearly half a century. J. Edgar Hoover's exact duties during World War I have long been a mystery, obscured by time, missing documentation, and perhaps some intentional camouflage.

He allowed almost no one in his home. His personal secretary, Helen Gandy, was one of the few he allowed. She began working with him when he was only 22, and continued after his death. She began destroying records after his death even before government officials could look at them. J. Edgar himself began destroying files a year before he died.

Only two black people were allowed into his home. A driver *(James Crawford),* who was a handyman at his house even after retiring, and a maid.

J. Edgar never married, and declared that he would never have children. He was afraid of showing his African American genes, and grew up hiding his ancestry. He hated himself.

After the death of his father, he became his mother's only companion and sole support.

J. Edgar left most of his estate to his long time companion, *Clyde Tolson.* He apparently was not close to his brother and sister. When he died, he cut his siblings and their children, out of his will.

In conclusion, I would say that, "What's done in the dark, will come to light."

When shown these pictures of
J.Edgar Hoover to most African
Americans they usually say, "I
knew it! I knew it! J. Edgar Hoover
has physical characteristics like a
biracial person.

William Allen T-L, the son of
William Hoover born in 1832
Clarence Allen T-R, grandson.
Lower right, J. Edgar Hoover,
Clarence Allen's second cousin.
{Family photo/FBI Files}

From The Mind Of A Ten Year Old.

Now we enter into the dream world of the author. Revealing stories told to the author by her Mother and Grandfather.

The author describes life and the history of a family, through the mind and eyes of a child.

The Oral History is depicted into a story by the author connecting real true-life documents, using dialect from that time.

She merges a 200-year Oral Family History with modern-day genealogical data to create a fascinating readable saga, which proves that history is never really, "black or white."

The love story!

1

I was wearing a little white cotton dress and had no shoes on my feet. It was the perfect dress to wear on a plantation. I believe my life story began on the plantation with my great-great grandmother. In a surprising way, so did another story about a man named John Edgar Hoover.

On this day, I still had a missing link to my childhood, but I started writing my first book anyway, calling it "Secret Fantasy." I thought this book was going to be about my own fantasies. It turned out not to be about that at all. The strangest things were going on. Things were coming out of my head about a slave from long ago named Emily Allen.

I began to daydream about a story that came to me about a plantation in Mississippi in 1809, and about slavery. I felt strange. A voice spoke to me.

"Close your mind to the world and relax," it said to me.

An uplifting feeling came over me; it felt like I was flying. Something very strange was happening. At first, I thought I was getting sleepy or maybe even sick. I could not stop thoughts from coming into my head. Then I realized that I wasn't afraid — I was going to the plantation to find out the truth about my past, and the next thing I knew, I drifted away.

Right away I heard someone calling out to me, but they were calling out the wrong name. Finally I could understand the name; Old Harry!

Who's Old Harry? I wondered.

A force was pulling on my body and I felt myself flying through thin air. When it stopped, I was wearing 18th century clothes, walking through a beautiful but undeveloped town. I found myself in a large crowd of screaming people.

I ran over to a counter where everybody was signing a

board, and I saw what looked like a roster. I noticed the date: the 27th day of November 1809. That's when I knew that I was back in time.

What was all the screaming about?

I looked up to see a large sign that read:

SLAVE AUCTION
SLAVES FOR SALE

I noticed something that looked like a stage. As I moved closer to see what it really was, I walked through the crowd but touched no one. I found that to be strange.

I reached out to touch the man next to me.

"Excuse me, sir, can you please tell me where I am?" I asked. He couldn't hear me, see me, or even feel my touch.

I looked around and realized that no one in the crowd was able to see me. There were no other women except for slave women. They were standing in line to be sold near the stage.

No one could see me, but I could see everything. I realized that I was there to watch. Everyone was looking at the white men with black whips in their hands. I wanted to see what it was that made them look so tall from the back of the room, so I approached. When I got closer I could see that it was a platform, built to raise the slave people high enough so that the crowd could see everyone for sale on display. They even had a podium for the speakers selling slaves.

The auction opened. The first slave to be sold was pushed onto the platform by one of the big men holding a black whip. She was pushed so hard that she fell down.

Seeing her fall, the white man started to hit her with the whip. I wanted to stop him, so I ran up on the platform. But I could do nothing. I had forgotten that no one could see me and I got really angry because I was so powerless. Then again, I realized that I was only there to watch, not to interfere.

When I looked up, a handsome white man had jumped onto the stage. He grabbed the big man, holding him by the arm with a strong grip.

"Sir, stop! You may damage the merchandise," he said firmly. He reached down and picked up a beautiful, thin, half-white, colored slave girl from the floor. She appeared more white-skinned than black.

I knew without a doubt that she was connected to me somehow because she looked so much like me as a young girl. A wonderful feeling come over me. Standing close, I looked into her eyes. She was beautiful; her eyes were green and she had long black hair. She was so pretty that I couldn't keep my eyes off of her, nor could I understand why her parents would sell her.

"Her parents aren't selling her!" I thought suddenly. Those white men took her from her parents to be sold as a slave.

I could tell that she was my relative alright. She had wide-set eyes and high rounded cheekbones. Her skin looked as white as any white person there, but she was being sold as a slave. The only thing that identified her as a colored girl was her hair, which was black and curly.

I noticed that all the slaves' skin colors differed. Some were dark and some were light. Some even looked white.

The auction began. It was very loud. It seemed unorganized to me, although the white men seemed to know exactly what they were doing. All the men in charge carried long black whips. They would hit the colored people on their backs to get them in some kind of order for display.

Slave-buying auctions were big business in the South. Slave owners were bidding for slaves like they were buying furniture for their homes. It sounded like a sports competition with all of the white men pushing and yelling at slaves. There were plantation owners from all across the southern states attending.

When they got things in order, they pushed the beautiful mulatto girl onto the display area. It was staged almost like a fashion show. She wore a soft white dress, through which men could see the shadow of her body. On her feet she wore what looked like white ballet slippers. Her breasts were the size of a mature woman, even though her face showed she could not have been more than 12 years old. When she stood up on the stage, everyone stopped talking to gaze at her.

Her beauty was absolutely electrifying. She was the most beautiful girl that I had seen in a long time. She appeared to be quite shy and frightened. I wanted to run up on stage to take her home and protect her, but it was impossible. I was only there to watch.

"Emily Allen! Birth date, November 27, 1793!"

"Oh my goodness, she is being sold on her birthday," I thought. They called out her specifications.

It was strange, looking at Emily, a girl I knew must be my great-great-grandmother, looking so young, innocent, and alive. I couldn't believe it. I was standing in front of her when she was just a girl.

"What a feeling this is!" I thought. I found myself trying to take Emily in my arms to protect her, but then again nothing happened. I kept forgetting I was only there to watch.

Then the auction started.

"We'll start the bidding for this fine young colored woman at $100," the auctioneer shouted. I was surprised. I knew that $100 was rather expensive for a slave.

These white men were taken by Emily's beauty and they all wanted her. They kept bidding and bidding until the price was sky-high. The bids began to sound like a countdown. Each time it went up, one plantation owner dropped out. Soon only three men were left in the contest for Emily.

"Three-fifty!" Shouted Master William Clifton Carson. He raised sheep on his plantation.

"Four hundred!" Countered Frederick Alexander Montgomery Jr., a cattle rancher who was related to Master Carson by his marriage to Helen (William Carson's sister). There were rumors that the Carson and Montgomery families had a falling out after Frederick and Helen got married, and the feud didn't help the bidding.

"Four-fifty," said Mr. Carson. He couldn't afford Emily, but he hated to let Mr. Montgomery win her.

"Four-seventy-five!" The latest bid from Mr. Montgomery forced Carson out of the race.

"Five hundred!" The newest bid came from the only bidder left besides Carson and Montgomery. Master Edward Dennis Hoover Jr.

Master Hoover raised horses. He married Master Montgomery's sister Charlotte. Since Mr. Montgomery saw that his brother-in-law wanted this slave badly, he yielded his bid to him for a future favor that he knew would come in handy one day. The bidding stopped at $500. Emily sold for the highest price ever. After that, slave auctions across the southern states increased the price of slaves.

I then remembered that it was Master Edward D. Hoover who ran onto the platform to save Emily from the business end of a whip. Master Montgomery remembered that too. I watched Mr. Hoover's face carefully. I could tell that winning the bid pleased him.

He was thinking about raising Emily as a white girl. I could read his face; he was wondering how he was going to keep anyone from knowing that she was colored.

"I'll cross that bridge when I get to it," he was thinking.

I decided that I would be part of the Hoover family while I was there, so I followed them from the auction to the plantation. Just as we were leaving, I heard Master Montgomery's voice.

"You owe me a favor, you know. I gave you that bid."

Master Hoover just nodded his head as he walked out to get into his horse carriage, keeping his arms around Emily. I walked with them to his fine horse carriage. He was especially kind to his new slave.

We all got in the carriage, and I watched him put his arms around Emily like she was his daughter. He had a blanket in the carriage and he wrapped it around her shoulders because she was shivering. It's hard to explain how I felt as I watched them. She was cold, and it probably was cold because Master Hoover wore a coat, but it was neither cold nor hot to me. I started to think that I was not among the living, but I stopped myself for fear that the fantasy would go away.

Soon I noticed there was a light-complected man driving the horses. I heard Master Hoover call him Old Harry. I found myself moving to the front of the carriage with him, remembering the name I'd heard calling me into the past. I knew that I wanted to know more about this man. I stared into his face as he told Old Harry to drive us to the ranch.

When his father died at the age of 72 in 1803, Master Hoover became the youngest slave owner in that part of the South. Old Harry was half-white, the son of William Carson Sr. and a slave named Sara. After Mr. Carson died, his wife, who found out about his indiscretions and didn't approve, sold Sara to Master Hoover's father. Sara was pregnant with Harry at the time, so he was born on the Hoover Ranch and lived there for 40 years. That's why they called him Old Harry. I could tell that Old Harry liked Emily when he first saw her, and so could Master Hoover.

When we got to the ranch Emily looked more relaxed and seemed to be less afraid of Master Hoover. He held her in his arms all the way to the ranch. He was talking to her about the way things operated on the Hoover Ranch Plantation.

"We're home now Emily," he said gently. "I want you to think of this ranch as your home, now and forever."

I moved back next to her in the carriage.

"You are only allowed to work inside the big house and not around the field slaves," he said. "You'll be the nanny to my children. You'll live in the nanny's quarters, which are a part of the big house."

Actually, the house was set up with two nanny's quarters; one inside the house, used while the nanny was breast-feeding, and the other outside, next to the house and connected to the porch, so that the nanny would have easy access to the children. This was done to keep her from actually living in the main part of the big house when the children were over two years old.

"Your job will be to look after the children's needs at all times," he explained. "They'll call you 'Mama.'"

He continued his discussion with Emily.

"We raise horses here at the ranch. We sell them on the market. We've got 50 slaves living here. They take care of the horses and the rest of the plantation.

You see the quarters over near the barn? That's where Willie stays. He's in charge of the health of the horses."

Willie and Old Harry had been on the Hoover's Ranch for decades. They were in charge of the slaves who took care of exercising, feeding, and cleaning the horses.

"We've got 10 other slaves to take care of the grounds and plant food in the garden," said Master Hoover. "We raise our own food. You'll like it here. We've got greens, tomatoes, okra, potatoes, beans, corn, peas, watermelon, and fruit trees."

Slaves did all the planting and picking of food from the garden. Old Harry was in charge of them and the horse carriage. He was the family's driver.

"We raise our own chickens, ducks, pigs, cows, and we even have a fishpond to catch fresh fish for dinner," Mr. Hoover continued. "Besides the livestock we've got pets; dogs, birds, and cats."

Twenty of the slaves were women; 10 kept the quarters clean, took care of their children, and helped prepare the food from the garden for the winter. They worked every day except Sunday.

"See now, over there's the church. All day Sunday, the slaves have church and celebrations." Master Hoover supervised Old Harry and Willie along with other field slaves to build the church on the plantation. It was nice, and could seat over 100 people.

Master Montgomery and Master Carson brought their families and slaves every Sunday to visit the Hoover Ranch. The slave women and the children rode in big horse buggies. The men walked or hung onto the sides of the buggies. The guards rode horses next to the slave buggies to make sure no one tried to run away.

They spent the whole day every Sunday celebrating a week's work done. The slaves believed that God was the reason for their good health. He enriched their work and they praised Him every week for it. Dressed in their Sunday best, they all praised God, sang and danced the whole day.

The Hoover Ranch was known for having "happy niggers." That's what other owners called them. The guards were there mainly to keep out strangers who might be snooping for information about the Hoovers. They were known to be a secretive family.

"Nobody's allowed to leave this place unless I say so," said Master Hoover. "I'm protecting you. You know that! I've got to guard my private life and my slaves."

Guards with guns surrounded the plantation gates.

"I gave orders they should shoot to kill anyone they find trespassing on my property," he said. "If anyone comes through that gate without permission, I told 'em to shoot first and ask questions later. But they aren't here on account of the slaves because I got good niggers."

He didn't tell Emily everything, one thing he never mentioned to her was, "The Hoover, Montgomery, and Carson." (HMC) club, which was started by the slave owners. If anyone wanted a person eliminated, they called an HMC meeting and helped each other do the job. They had control of the community because they were owners of almost everything in town. They influenced the sheriff and the business owners, who paid the HMC Club to let them stay in business. Anyone that got in their way was removed and never seen or found again.

On Sundays, the HMC Club would spend the day together in the big house. They had their own party and dressed in their best attire. The club members and their families sat on the porch while Sister Harriet, a slave woman, would sing those good old gospel hymns. Sister Harriet was very spiritual. None of the masters had any sexual dealings with her because they feared her praying a bad spell on them and their families.

Sister Harriet was 17 years old and she was married to the church minister, Pastor John Martin, who was 23 years old.

There was something unholy about the HMC Club. Master William Carson Sr. started sex gambling games with his slaves. These games were played with slave people like they were animals. It was like a horse race and the HMC Club had them about twice a month. They called it "The Climaxing First Game." A slave master would pick two strong male field slaves and two female field slaves, and use them in a sex game, taking bets and bringing in big money. The slaves had to have sex in front of a group of white men in the barn who paid money to see this show. The slaves had to perform like they were in a boxing ring. It lasted all day and sometimes all night by candlelight.

The couples would start out fully dressed in the center of the barn.

"Let's go, get ready and let the games begin!"

Master Carson always started his game the same way. At the signal the slaves were to start kissing and touching each other. They'd take off one piece of clothing after the next until they were undressed down to nudity. The crowd acted like it was a ball game the way they cheered them on. It was all part of the show. When the male slave's got an erection, that started the bidding. Once the white men made a choice that set their bids, it was recorded in writing and couldn't be changed. To win, the white men had to predict which couple climaxed first.

If the slaves didn't perform they could be killed, and they knew it, because they'd heard that Master William Carson Sr. did have a couple killed once. When they didn't obey the rules, he up and killed them right in front of everyone. That was his orders.

Emily and Master Hoover still sat in the carriage near Old Harry.

"Isn't she a might young to be a nanny?" Asked Old Harry. This was the moment their friendship changed. He noticed that Old Harry was showing an interest in Emily.

"Mind your own business," he snapped. Then he turned to him and looked him in the eye.

"Don't you go near her unless I tell you to," he muttered.

Emily heard them arguing about her and began to feel

upset again. I could see her fear coming back. Master Hoover slipped his arm around her.

"You stay clear of Old Harry...for that matter, don't you go near the field slaves; none of them." He went on a bit to make his point. After he finished talking to her, he got out of the carriage and helped her down. I felt kind of bad because no one could help me out of the carriage. No one could see me.

Old Harry's feelings were hurt and he did not talk anymore after that. He just turned and went to work. He cleaned the horses up and took them to eat.

I took a look around the grounds. It was so pretty. The trees and grass were as green as emeralds.

Soon I found myself running through the fields like a child, heading toward the horse stables. I wanted a horse ever since I was very young and the Hoover horses were the best looking horses I'd ever seen. They looked like the horses you would see in a picture book, with rippling muscles in their chests and proud, flaring nostrils. I guess that is why the Hoover Ranch Plantation's reputation was so good. The slave children fed the horses and adults groomed them. Hoover Ranch was known as the best horse ranch in that part of the South.

I could hardly believe places were so beautiful in this century. It was like something that you would see in a painting.

The big house was beautiful too. It was white, trimmed in gray. There were some little houses built out back of the big house that looked like small doll-houses. When I looked at those little houses, they put me in the mind of a dwarf community. The little houses were built for the slaves' quarters. They were all painted white and looked very neat. After I collected myself, I looked and saw Master Hoover talking to Madam Charlotte at the front door of the mansion. She was opening the door for Emily. I ran as fast as I could because I was afraid I would miss something.

It was great to be on a fascinating trip like this. I had never encountered anything like it in my life before.

I noticed Emily and Madam Charlotte looking deep into

each other's eyes. This was strange to me. I had a feeling they wanted to be a part of each other's lives. I still didn't fully understand what was going on with these two women. While we were standing at the door, I looked at Madam Charlotte Hoover.

"What a stunningly beautiful woman she is! She seems sweet too," I thought.

Master Hoover seemed surprised at the way Charlotte took to Emily. It was almost as though she wanted her for a daughter. It was true that she could pass for white, which is what he really wanted. He knew his wife might never have a child of her own. She had an illness that made childbirth dangerous for her.

When I entered the big house, I saw how beautiful it was. The furniture was antique. I love antique things. Their toilet was out in back of the house. They called it an outhouse. There were old kerosene lamps that were made out of brass and glass. I was quite impressed and surprised at the bright light that shone into the room. I again felt that I had somehow left my body, and entered into strange lands.

I heard Madam Charlotte and Master Hoover talking, so I moved closer.

"A nanny? She can't nurse our babies until she has a baby herself," she was saying.

"She'll have a baby with one of the slaves," he said. He was thinking he'd impregnate her himself.

"She looks like a baby herself! She's too young to bear children. I won't let any man touch her at all until she's older." She saw that her husband was about to object so she put her foot down.

"If we're going to keep her here at Hoover Ranch, that's how it's going to be. This girl is too young to be a nanny and if you don't like it you can take her back to the auction right now and sell her for an older woman," said Madam Charlotte.

She saw that Emily had become very sad. I noticed tears running down her face.

"Furthermore, I don't think we should start our family just yet," she said. She knew that her talk about sending Emily back to the auction had upset her. She felt bad about hurting her feelings, but it had to be done in order to get Master Hoover to see things her way. Then she put her arms around her little body to comfort her.

Emily seemed to like Madam Charlotte from the start. She wanted desperately to stay on the ranch.

"I'll take her in as if I gave birth to her," she said. Seeing the look on Master Hoover's face, she knew he hoped for something else with her.

"I will take care of her for four years, until she is old enough to become a nanny," said Madam Charlotte. She was thinking that by then she would be ready to marry and have her own children. He seemed confused and a bit unhappy, but he knew he really didn't have a choice if he wanted to have her some day. His wife laid down the law about the care of her and what was going to take place.

I was surprised by the way he accepted her rules, but then I realized how badly he wanted Emily. Madam Charlotte wanted to take care of her as if she were her own daughter. She did not want her to end up like Sweet Anna.

Sweet Anna lived on the Montgomery Plantation. She was used for sex by all of the masters in the club any time they wanted it. That's how she got her name, Sweet Anna. She was known as every man's "Bed Warmer."

Madam Charlotte thought it would be wrong to put her out with the field slaves for the taking, and maybe Master Hoover's use as well. In her mind, she had picked Old Harry to father Emily's children. He was a mulatto slave, and he was treated like a white man on the Hoover Ranch. He didn't work like the field slaves — he was their boss. Master Hoover left him in charge because he trusted Old Harry. What Madam Charlotte didn't know was that her husband bought Emily for one reason; to become a bed warmer for himself. She didn't know that her beauty and breasts fascinated him.

"According to her papers, she's 16 years old. Sixteen-year-old slave girls are having babies and marrying if they are healthy. She looks plenty healthy and old enough to take on her duties," said Master Hoover.

"Stop right there." Madam Charlotte wasn't having any more of this.

"She is no more than 12 years old. Even if she was 16, she isn't big enough to have any children, or get married. You can take her back to the auction and swap her for someone older or go by my rules. That's it! I'm not letting any man take advantage of a child."

Well, she won the argument. When I heard that, I knew he was going to let her do whatever she wanted. He had fallen in love with Emily from the start and he wanted her body badly. He'd wait if he had to, but he was determined to have her. She was a pretty girl. I could see why he wanted to keep her around. He knew that in a few years she would be a magnificent looking, beautiful woman.

It seemed to me, Madam Charlotte liked the fact that Emily could pass for white because she wanted a daughter.

During the next four years Madam Charlotte teamed up with Miss Lilly, her housemaid and cook, to teach Emily about the facts of life. And they taught her well. They taught her everything that she needed to know, or everything a young girl should know, before getting married. It was fun watching. They taught her how to cook, clean, speak properly, read, and make love to any man (or her future husband, as Madam Charlotte thought). She learned how to become a proper young lady.

Madam Charlotte had the nanny's quarters inside the house turned into a classroom. This was where Emily learned to read, and it was also where she slept.

A secret book was passed among the relatives in Madam Charlotte's family, called "Sex Can Be Exciting and Good." She had gotten it from her sister-in-law, Helen, who received the book from a relative who lived in England. Madam and Emily read the book together.

Everyone was talking about the big wedding that would take place when Emily turns 20. Madam Charlotte made a rule that she was not allowed anywhere near Old Harry until her coming-out party. That was just fine with Master Hoover because he had a "master plan." For four years, the only times Emily saw Old Harry were through the window as he came and went with Master Hoover.

Master Hoover tried to go into Emily's room many times late at night, but Madam Charlotte always caught him.

"I heard a noise," he'd say, or "I just wanted to say good-night."

"Hmmm. Well, she can't be disturbed because she has an early morning class tomorrow," Madam would reply. His wife always seemed to be watching him and it made him angry, but he would just go back to his library and read.

2

November 26, 1813 was the day Master Hoover had anxiously awaited for four long years. Emily was coming out from the protection of her madam, and he was ready. Her coming-out party was on her birthday, the anniversary of the day she was put up for sale.

Madam thought that her coming-out party was to be the day before her wedding, which she had already arranged. The party would be a noisy celebration with music, dancing, and lots of food, held in the big house. She invited Old Harry, who was to be the only slave allowed.

Master was not happy about Old Harry. He was happy about the four years being over. He was just aching to touch Emily. No one knew about his master plan. He intended to put it into play right after the party.

What he didn't know was that Madam Charlotte had a master plan of her own.

Years earlier, when the Montgomery and Carson families had their falling out, everyone talked about how old Master Carson had once cheated Master Montgomery Sr. out of a bid at the auction. Master Montgomery never forgave him. Their friendship had ended right then and there.

The resulting feud interfered with a romance between Helen Carson's brother, Percy, and Frederick Montgomery's sister, Charlotte. Percy was in love with Charlotte in high school and asked her to marry him. Her father wouldn't hear of his daughter marrying a Carson. He put a stop to it right away by arranging a marriage with Master Hoover. This deeply upset Percy, so he left Mississippi and never came back until the death of his mother.

Master Hoover waited four years for this night. However,

Madam Charlotte had been waiting ever since high school.

"Percy will be in town," confided her sister-in-law, Helen. "He is planning to see you at Emily's coming-out party if you'll just send him an invitation," Helen said.

Percy Carson was still in love with Madam Charlotte, and I believe that she was still in love with him. She intended to put her master plan in motion that night.

It was almost time for the party and everyone was busy. The Hoovers invited all of their friends to attend this beautiful event.

"My sister from Virginia will be here and we're throwing a party for her," Master Hoover told people. Of course, Emily was to be his "sister." Most of their friends knew the truth, but they wanted to put this story out into the community so they could pass her as white. Outside of the Hoover Plantation, her ethnicity was kept a secret, except for close friends. Keeping secrets for each other was part of their vows in the HMC Club.

Madam Charlotte bought a stunning red dress for Emily to wear. It fit close to her body, and a deep neckline as it hung to the floor, showing off her body and breasts.

She went into Emily's room for their last talk. She stood in the doorway looking electrifying in that red dress. Madam sat down to talk. She had grown into a lovely young woman and she was ready to start her job as nanny. As she looked at her, Madam felt so proud. Just like a mother would look at her daughter.

"You look beautiful, dear," she said as Emily smoothed her skirts, and sat on the bed near her.

Old Harry was looking handsome too, as he waited and wondered how his lovely pretend bride was going to look. Old Harry knew that this was part of Master Hoover's master plan for Emily.

"You'll never get close to her," Master Hoover had informed him.

But Old Harry would have to wait just a bit longer before he could look at her, because she wanted one last talk with Madam. It was important to her to have this talk before her party. She sat next to Madam and when she began to talk, she spoke from her heart.

"I want to thank you for being like a mother to me. Since I was born a slave, it was a lucky day when Master Hoover bought me from that auction and you decided to raise me as your daughter. When he brought me to this ranch, and to a new mother, my life became worth living." she said.

Madam was happy to hear her say those nice things to her. But Emily wasn't done yet.

"It's time for me to take care of the beautiful Hoover children that you're going to have," she said. As she spoke, Madam began to cry. With tears running down her face, she reached out for her hand.

"Emily, you are the daughter that I wanted many years ago, that I thought I couldn't have."

Emily smiled, happy that they felt such affection for each other. Then they hugged. At last they were ready to go into the party room to meet all of the Hoover's friends. They were told that she was Master Hoover's sister.

"What are you doing telling everyone that?" Madam asked Master Hoover.

"This is the news for the community," he said. "It's my way of protecting Emily's future. She'll pass for white if she needs to."

Old Harry, Master Hoover, and all their friends were waiting expectantly in the big party room. The door opened at the top of the stairs and Madam Charlotte came down. Everyone stopped and looked at her. She was exquisite. Suddenly, she stopped at the bottom of the stairs, surprised by the sight of her childhood sweetheart, Percy Carson. He was standing in attendance as if he was there to pick her up for a date. Even though she had invited him, she didn't think he would really come. When she pulled herself together, she looked into her friends' faces.

"Ladies and gentlemen, please look this way." She paused dramatically.

"I am honored to present and introduce you to Emily

Allen, my sister-in-law from Virginia!" Like a vision, Emily appeared at the top of the stairs. The room immediately silenced and the guests gazed at her beauty. She walked down the stairs elegantly, like a queen. I then turned and looked at Master Hoover. I could tell he was stunned and speechless because he could not keep his eyes off of her. He stared at her all night, even while he was dancing in the arms of his own wife.

As they danced closely, I noticed an odd look on Madam Charlotte's face. I then realized that she felt him as he had become aroused. What she didn't know was he was watching Emily behind her back. She started to become aroused herself from the feeling of his body touching hers. She wanted to leave the party for a few minutes to make love to him.

"We have all night to be together," he whispered. "If we leave the room it might upset Emily. After all, this is her first party. She needs our support, don't you think?"

"Yes, you're right my dear," she said, thinking it was good that he was pleased and cooperating with her plans.

Still dancing, she took the opportunity to talk to Master about Emily and Old Harry's future.

"I want to thank you for your approval of Old Harry's marriage to Emily," she began. "She will make him a good wife."

When she said that, I could tell that she was going on too much about Old Harry and Emily. He was starting to get jealous. Pretty soon I was afraid he'd be boiling with anger.

"Edward isn't this wonderful? When Emily and Harry are married tomorrow, they'll be part of our family!"

Her words about Old Harry being part of the family made him angry and he stopped dancing.

"It's *not* wonderful. Old Harry will never be a part of us," he snorted. "Old Harry is a slave on the ranch. He works here, and that's all."

"Sshhh! You're making a scene in front of everyone," she said.

"And furthermore..."

She stopped him because she didn't want anyone to hear. "Could you join me in the library?" She asked quickly.

I followed them into the library because I wanted to see if Master Hoover was going to tell her about his master plan. He was as angry as could be. When they reached the library, he exploded.

"No more!" Scene or no scene, he was beginning to raise his voice. "I've gone along with your shit too long!"

She was trying to get him to lower his voice, and he did, but he was furious.

"Four f*ing years I've put up with your ideas, because I paid a lot of money for that slave," he hissed.

I was just as shocked as Madam Charlotte. I think he was jealous of Old Harry being able to put his hands on Emily while they were dancing.

Old Harry was treated special because his mother raised Master. He and Old Harry were like brothers for two years. Since Master Carson Sr. fathered Old Harry, he looked so much like a white man. He was the only slave at the party, and being a slave was kept a secret from the invited guests.

"Edward, Emily's wedding is tomorrow, and you are going to spoil it for her if you keep on acting this way in front of our friends," said Madam.

"I don't give a flying, you know what, about friends. This shit has got to stop! It's gone on long enough." His voice carried right through the library door.

Everyone at the party stopped dancing. They were surprised at what was going on. None of it made any sense to anyone. But I thought this was a part of his master plan. Madam was in a state of shock and speechless. He was just going on and on.

"If my father knew about this, I know he would be turning over in his grave!" He started walking out the door. I was standing right in front of him in the way. He walked right through me. It frightened me so much, it felt like he knocked me down. Then he stopped and turned around. I think he felt me, but I didn't feel him. He had a strange look on his face.

I must remember that I can't get too involved emotionally in their lives, because this time I almost became a part of them. "If that happens that can be dangerous," I thought. I knew that if that happened it might cause my death back in my lifetime, which was supposed to be in the future from here.

I must be careful and remember that I am just here to watch, I reminded myself. After he passed through me I got up. I noticed that he was standing there collecting his thoughts.

"This shit stops now! He continued. I want Emily out of this house tonight and put in the nanny's quarters out back, where she belongs." He started to walk off, but changed his mind.

"Also, I want her moved before I get back home tonight. She'll stay there until she is needed in the nanny's quarters in the main house." He started walking out of the room again as I was just getting up from the floor. When I looked up, he walked right through me again, but this time I felt it as well as he did. Oh boy, I knew that got him really mad this time. Then he turned around and glared at her.

"You know, I feel the presence of my father's spirit in this room and he is not pleased with me at all." There I was, not thinking, just standing there in the way, shocked and surprised by what he was saying. Again, I was not paying attention. He knocked me onto the floor going out the door. I got up fast this time because I wanted to follow him to the party room to see what he was going to do or say to all of his friends.

I watched him go directly over to get his hat and coat. He was looking so angry. It was sad because everyone, including Emily and Old Harry, heard them arguing. Not one person knew what they were arguing about except me, but they really wanted to know. They couldn't hear the exact words because Madam Charlotte closed the door to protect their privacy. The party stopped. Everyone was standing around with a surprised look on their faces.

"Get the horse and carriage. I'm going into town," he said abruptly. He was talking to Old Harry. There was silence for a moment.

Madam was in the library crying. Emily heard her and went in to see about her. When she passed by Master Hoover standing in the foyer waiting for the carriage to come around, her eyes showed fear. He looked angry. He couldn't look at her. He knew that he had strong feelings for her and he feared that his deep sexual feelings might be aroused. As she passed by him, he smelled the scent of her body and it was very sensuous to him. Her tempting aroma caused him to get aroused all over again and he quickly moved into another room to get his mind on something else.

Sometimes I felt like a ghost since none of them could see me and all those people never knew I was there. I was standing there looking, and I could see what no one else saw. I could tell Master was highly susceptible and influenced by her beauty. The smell of her body turned on the indulgence of his appetite and he wanted her badly.

Everyone seemed to think that the argument was about Madam's old boyfriend because of the affectionate look she'd given him when she first saw him. I knew that Master hadn't even see her look at Percy Carson because he was too busy thinking about Emily. I think she may have worried that he'd seen her and she thought maybe that upset him. After all, a good-looking man like Percy would make any man jealous.

The food was still in the kitchen. Miss Lilly was waiting to serve the food. I watched Master Hoover when he went into the kitchen to talk to her.

I wanted to know if this was part of his master plan? So I followed him into the kitchen.

"Put the food away," I heard him tell Miss Lilly.

When she looked surprised, he grew impatient.

"I said, put it away! Use it for the big celebration in the slave quarters tomorrow." He didn't say wedding. He said, *celebration*. He knew something was going to interfere with the wedding, but he wasn't telling anyone.

"Help get Emily moved to the outside nanny's quarters. Do it now. Before I get back home," he said.

"Yes, sir," said Miss Lilly.

"Your carriage is ready to go, sir." Old Harry had come into the kitchen.

"That's fine. Wait for me outside," he replied. He turned to Miss Lilly.

"Come with me," he ordered. She followed him to the library where Madam and Emily were.

"Emily, go with Miss Lilly now. You'll be getting your things ready to move into the nanny's quarters." He didn't look at his wife's eyes.

"I'll be going into town for awhile. No need to wait up," he said to Madam.

"I don't understand. What about Emily's party?..." She couldn't understand why he'd ruin Emily's party with his jealousy.

"Why are you so upset? Please don't walk out," she said.

"The slaves around here will be treated like slaves from now on. They are not family." These were her husband's last words to her that night. He turned on his heels and walked out, interrupting a buzz of gossip that had erupted among the guests.

"The party is over. Time to leave now," he said curtly.

Shocked, everyone collected their belongings and left, except Percy Carson. I was the only one that saw him slip onto the dark porch, where he hid himself from the Master. None of the other guests knew he was back there. Not even the Madam.

Later on, rumors would fly and tongues would wag about that night. After everyone had gone, Madam was alone. When she saw Percy, she was so pleased that he stayed. It was said that the guards saw something going on in the Master's bedroom window late that night. They saw Percy when he slipped away in the dark later on.

They kept her secret, but she didn't know that they all knew. The guards told the rumor to Helen Carson about her brother Percy being in Master Hoover's bedroom window making passionate love to Madam Charlotte. Helen kept that secret to herself. I think they all felt sorry for the Madam for the way Master Hoover treated her at the party.

I decided to follow along with Master and Old Harry. I wanted to see this until the end. I walked with him to the carriage. When we got there I jumped in first because I was excited to find out what his master plan was. I soon found out that it was a mistake to jump in the carriage first because when he got in, he sat right in my lap. I couldn't feel him sitting in my lap, so I pulled myself from under him, but to my surprise he felt me when I did that. I could tell by the look on his face. He sat there in the carriage for a moment, as if he was wondering what was happening to him. He never said a word; he just sat there with this perplexed look on his face.

"Just drive around," he finally said to Old Harry.

"What's wrong, Master?" Old Harry was worried about him.

"I've got everything all worked out," he said. Even though I had a feeling about his plan, I was still surprised at what he said next.

"Old Harry, you are not ever going to be with Emily in any way, except like a friend," he said. "I've decided to take over the plantation the way my father taught me. Slaves on the Hoover Ranch don't act like slaves, and that's going to change as of now."

Old Harry was even more disappointed at what came next.

"Remember what my father said about you and me before he died? He said I should learn to treat you like a slave, not a brother. Father said one day you would become my slave." Master looked him in the eye.

"You a nigger, not a white man. You just remember that."

Old Harry didn't say a word. He just kept on driving.

"You aren't my friend or my brother. You disobey my orders, you'll be sold at the auction."

I sat there very surprised, just like Old Harry. Master began to act different when he realized that his feelings for Emily were real. He changed when he saw that she had become a beautiful woman.

We rode around going nowhere in particular, listening to

him talk to Old Harry about the new rules.

"Drive to the Montgomery Plantation," he finally ordered.

When we got there they were just getting home from the party themselves. I got out of the carriage with Master Hoover.

"Wait in the carriage," he ordered. Old Harry sat quietly; there was nothing else he could do.

I wanted to see what he was going to do. I noticed that when Master Montgomery saw him coming to the door he came out on the porch to meet him. Maybe neither one wanted any wives around. I was right there with them when he got started on his master plan. I had a feeling that this was going to be an interesting night.

"I need another favor," he began.

"You know, I was just thinking about you, because I am in need of a favor from you too," said Mr. Montgomery.

"Good. Here's the thing." I crept closer so I could hear. "I want Old Harry to stay out back with your slave woman tonight." He needed to get rid of him, not just to keep him from the big celebration the next day, but also because it would help with his master plan, so he could get through to Emily easier.

"That's fine. Your boy can stay at my place for the night." Montgomery had things in mind too.

"I want to go back to the Hoover Ranch with you tonight because I need a bed warmer," Montgomery said. "I've been looking at Miss Lilly. Been wanting to have my way with her for months."

Master had to think about this.

"I want some of her real bad tonight," he said. His wife, Helen, was standing right at the door and I think she heard him telling Master that she was on the rag, so he needed Miss Lilly. I stood there surprised to hear those two men with their own wives, making deals to use slave women as bed warmers like that.

The Master was happy because his plan worked out. He headed back toward the carriage.

"Old Harry, I want you to help Master Montgomery with

some work tomorrow." This was a lie. "You'll have to stay the night with Sweet Anna."

Harry wondered about the so-called wedding the next day, but Master Hoover settled that.

"Because of the celebration tomorrow, I won't be able to get you back on time." Old Harry knew this was part of the big master plan. There wasn't much he could do but just go along with it.

"You come back tomorrow after the celebration. Wait 'till it's dark." He didn't want him around until he needed the carriage again and it was time for his next plan. Old Harry didn't ask any questions. He just got out of the carriage like Master Hoover told him to do, then walked toward the slave quarters to see Sweet Anna.

Master Montgomery was telling another version of plans to his wife.

"Helen, I'm taking Edward home. He's going to leave his carriage here. I've got some work for his boy in the morning, so Old Harry will take the carriage home tomorrow night. I'll be back late; probably go out for a beer. No need to wait up."

They had told so many lies, I wondered if they even remembered them all. They got into the Montgomery carriage and headed toward the Hoover Ranch, laughing and talking about sex and women all the way. I got in the back of the carriage so I could hear them. They rode together so they could talk about the master plan and Emily. That was what I wanted to hear.

"When I get back to the ranch, I plan to take Emily," said Master. "I've got to win her confidence. Figured the best way is to make Old Harry look bad in her eyes."

I began to understand that he had it arranged all along. Now that Emily was out back in her new quarters, no one could stop him from getting to her.

He waited those four long years to be able to touch her body. Finally, he was going to carry out his master plan. They pulled up in back of the house where Old Harry always parked the carriage. I watched them take the horses off the carriage and secure them in the barn, just like Old Harry did.

He took Mr. Montgomery to Miss Lilly's quarters.

"Where's Emily?" He said the moment she opened the door for him.

"Yes sir, she's all moved into the nanny's quarters out back, just like you told me to do, Master." Then she saw Mr. Montgomery standing there in back of him and wondered what he wanted.

"You need anything else, Master?" She asked, hoping it wasn't what she was thinking.

"My friend, Mr. Montgomery, took a liking to you and wants to visit with you for awhile," he said.

"Now Master Hoover, you know Willie Carson is my man, and you promised me a long time ago that you would never do this to me." She was very surprised at Master Hoover. "Master, we are just finishing up supper," she added; hoping he'd go away. I watched as he pushed his way into her quarters and Willie was just sitting there on the floor eating.

"Sorry. Willie has to leave now." Before she could say another word, he continued. "If you like having Willie around the ranch, you had better get him out of here now, and be a real good girl to my friend here." Miss Lilly sure didn't want to be there without Willie, so she asked him to leave.

"If you aren't good to Mr. Montgomery, you'll get a beating from both of us. And the next day, you'll find yourself at the auction," he said. She right away told Willie to go to his quarters. Willie didn't speak a word; he got up from the floor and went to his quarters.

Miss Lilly was very surprised because Master Hoover had never done anything like this to her. When she was alone with Mr. Montgomery, who was a big man, he picked up her petite half-white body and laid her on the padding and blankets she used for a bed on the floor. It was already made for Willie. Mr. Montgomery couldn't wait. He started touching and kissing her breasts, then taking off her clothes. She didn't try to stop him; she let him have his way with her like a good girl, just as Master said. Mr. Montgomery must have wanted her badly because as soon as he entered her body he reached a climax.

She was glad of that. She wanted it to be over. When it was over she thought he would leave, but he didn't.

"I tell you girl you shoo' have some good stuff," he said. Then he turned over, fell asleep and began snoring. Boy, he was snoring so loud until I thought it sounded like a big horse snorting! Miss Lilly looked at him and tried to get his arms from around her neck. He went to sleep holding her in his arms and I watched her trying to get loose. Every time she started to move, that old goat would open his eyes. She had to stay there until he woke up. She didn't get to see Willie any more that night. I really wanted to help her, but I couldn't.

I was surprised when I turned to leave, because I caught Master Hoover watching them too. He was looking through the window. When he left Miss Lilly's, he went straight to Emily's quarters and knocked on her door. I ran to catch up with him because I did not want to miss anything. When she opened the door she seemed surprised to see him. She had on a sexy nightgown. She looked like she was looking for someone to come by.

"It's late and something must have happened," she thought. She wondered why she hadn't heard Old Harry bring the carriage back. She had gone to bed and was almost asleep.

"Oh my, Master Hoover, are you still angry?" she said. He stepped into her quarters, put his arm around her, and walked with her toward her bed, sitting her down.

"No, Emily I'm not angry anymore, I wasn't angry with you anyway."

"But Master, who made you so angry?"

Back came the master plan.

"I was angry with Old Harry. He is not doing what is expected of him around here. We planned for him to be your husband, but he doesn't seem to be happy about it."

"What did he do?" he was not listening to her, because he was all caught up in her beauty. He found himself sitting just looking into her eyes and wanting her so badly. He couldn't help himself; he took her into his arms and kissed her gently. She was confused by his actions and she wasn't sure what to do. Then he stopped kissing her and acted like something was wrong.

"I have something to tell you before tomorrow," he said. I was on my way outside, but I heard him talking about what was supposed to be her wedding day, so I decided to stay.

She looked into his eyes for answers.

"Did something happen to Old Harry?" She asked.

"He is alright, but he doesn't want to marry you."

She seemed sad at first, and then angry.

"Does he have another lady that he wants to marry?" She asked. He was happy to hear her ask that question.

"It appears so," he replied. "He has a field slave who lives on Mr. Montgomery's place named Sweet Anna that he has been seeing for years."

Now that was not entirely the truth because all the slave men around town used Sweet Anna if Master Montgomery allowed it. The white men used her for a bed warmer whenever Master Montgomery wanted to give her to them. Sweet Anna was a beautiful woman. All the white men called her a "high yellow nigger." They all loved having sex with her, and Old Harry was no exception. Those men said she had good sex, but the women called her the town's ho. Knowing all this, he went on explaining his version of things to Emily.

"Old Harry took me to a business meeting at the Montgomery place tonight. Then he went to see Sweet Anna. When I got ready to come home I found Old Harry in bed with her. That's when he told me how he felt about you. He said he didn't want any woman but Sweet Anna. Then he wanted to know if he had to marry you, even though he didn't want to." He was really making up a lot of lies just to get on the good side of Emily.

"Old Harry asked me to tell you that he was not interested in marrying you; he's in love with Sweet Anna." He embellished these lies with several more details. He went on to say, "I'm very angry with Old Harry. I have decided to sell him at the slave auction tomorrow."

"Please, don't sell him because I'm not interested in marrying any man if he doesn't want me," she said. "No one should be punished for wanting to be with the person they love."

It was clear to me that Master Hoover felt the same should apply to him, because he loved her. I felt him thinking that he wanted to be married to her, but he knew that wasn't possible.

"Well, Old Harry wanted to stay the night with Sweet Anna, and I'm going to send him away," he said. He stood up. Emily jumped up in dismay.

"Oh no, Master Hoover please don't send him away. I just don't want a man that doesn't want me," she repeated, with tears filling her eyes.

This pleased Master Hoover. He never wanted to send Old Harry away anyway, but he wanted her to think he was protecting her.

They stood together, looking at each other, their eyes filled with emotion.

Emily had been preparing to become a wife and a mother for four years, and she wanted to make love. She was taught how to make passionate love to the man intended for her. Madam Charlotte told her to enjoy having sex while trying to conceive her children.

I took a look up toward the big house and noticed there were no lights on. I felt like they were getting ready to have sex. I didn't want to be watching, but I was inside the nanny's quarters. Everything was moving so fast. When I turned back to look at them, they were still standing, but in each other's arms holding each other with a great degree of passion.

She had been looking forward to using some of the techniques on Old Harry that she learned from her book. But, Old Harry wasn't going to be a husband to her. She remembered the book had drawings of love-making showing many different positions. I was fascinated with the knowledge that she had obtained about being sexy and making love. She was ready to use it on her man. She just never thought that her man would be Master Hoover.

"What should I tell Madam Charlotte?" She asked. She seemed more worried about hurting Madam than she was about Old Harry.

"We're not going to tell her anything. Just let her think you're getting married to Old Harry," he said.

This was part of his master plan.

"Madam Charlotte wants to have a baby by the end of the year," he explained, going on to the next step of his plan. "That means you'll need to be impregnated right away in order to be ready to breast-feed her baby. I'll father your first child, but you must never tell her, or anyone else for that matter. This will be our secret."

"Madam Charlotte has been good to me, and I don't want to disappoint her," she said.

He knew he had to convince her that it was alright to father her child. He also had to arrange it so that absolutely no one could be told about it. It would be the secret for many centuries. He was proud of his ability to manipulate and privately called himself "The Master of Deceit."

"But Master," said Emily, "what if I am asked who is the father of my child? What should I say?"

"Tell them it is your husband Old Harry's child. He is the only slave on this place that looks white," said Master Hoover. "This will protect Madam Charlotte's feelings."

I started to leave, but I wanted to see if it would really happen, so I found a seat on the floor. I noticed that Emily was starting to get aroused just by looking at him. He was a very sexy and good-looking man.

Madam Charlotte taught her how to keep her body clean and sexy with a few oils and lubricants. She even taught her how to masturbate when she was alone and needed to be loved. I found it to be fascinating watching her teach Emily. Now the time had come. She was actually going to use the knowledge that she learned with a man for the first time, only Madam thought it would be Old Harry.

Master Hoover told Emily that Old Harry was in on their secret; which was a lie. He knew that he would need to tell Madam Charlotte that Emily and Old Harry were married so he planned to go ahead with the fake wedding. She didn't realize that Old Harry wouldn't even be there. Master had been dying to get to Emily and he couldn't wait any longer.

He pulled her tighter into his arms, holding her very close to his body. He began to kiss her and touch her breasts, and soon he was all over her body. She was beginning to get aroused and enjoy it. When he touched her between her legs, he cupped his entire hand over her vagina and began moving it up and down gently. This was exciting and arousing to her and her excitement sent feelings of titillation all through his body.

They both became so aroused and couldn't wait to make love. They made love passionately as they held each other close for the first time.

It was refreshing to me to see how passionate they were, but it seemed to be over as soon as it got started. Her face looked worried about something.

"What's wrong?" He asked.

"It seems wrong somehow, the way I feel in my heart for you, but I can't stop myself from wanting more of you."

He was happy to hear her say that because he knew that he wanted more of her too.

"I don't like lying to my Madam like this because we have never lied to each other before," she worried. "I love Madam Charlotte because she took me in and raised me as her own daughter and taught me everything I know."

"This isn't wrong, because we love each other," he said. "As long as she doesn't know, everything will be fine."

She seemed unsure, so he added more deceit.

"Emily, if you don't do this for Madam, she will never be able to have a child of her own. You must understand! She can't relax about having a child of her own unless she thinks you are having a child, but Old Harry doesn't want you."

Well, he had convinced her to have his child, and she started to smile. I didn't want to leave the room, even though I thought that I should, but I loved watching them make love. After all, I was sent there just to watch. I watched her make passionate love to him, until they were satisfied. This time she was not sad after making love to him; she thought everything was great the second time around.

"We aren't hurting anyone if we keep it a secret," she told herself.

My goodness, I thought, he is teaching her how to be as deceitful as himself!

"You are absolutely right," he said. "Everything works out for everyone this way." He held her in his arms.

"I promise that I'll always look out for you and our children," he said.

As I stood there watching and listening to them, I knew without a doubt that they were in love with each other. That wasn't hard to figure out. I could tell by the way they looked at each other and by the way they made love to each other. I always believed that Emily had fallen in love with Master Hoover from the beginning. He was a very appealing man. Tall and thin, with light blue eyes, brown hair, nice teeth, and he was romantic.

"This is my way of thanking him for being so kind," she thought. Getting pregnant will be my gift to Madam Charlotte. After convincing herself that they were doing the right thing, and making love to complete satisfaction, she was happy. I think that she loved making love to Master Hoover as much as he loved making love to her.

After they finished, it was late and he prepared to leave her. He had to arrange the big secret that he was planning for her the next day. His master plan wasn't complete yet.

Emily was excited about the big celebration ahead of her, come morning. By now she knew it was a celebration instead of her wedding. She thought of it as celebrating her love for Master Hoover. Only Madam Charlotte thought it was her wedding day.

"Have you ever had sex with anyone before me?" He asked before he left.

"Once, my father, who was my mother's master, took

me."

He was surprised because she was just a girl when he bought her.

"How old were you," He asked.

"I was only 10 years old. It was painful," she said. She smiled at him. "But it was not painful with you Master. It was wonderful!"

"How did you know just what to do?"

"Madam Charlotte taught me everything about sex."

This made him wonder because his wife did not make love to him like that.

It was very late so he got dressed to leave and kissed her good-night. Just as he left her quarters he saw Master Montgomery leaving Miss Lilly's quarters, getting into his horse carriage.

"Montgomery must have had a good time with Miss Lilly, the way he was smiling," he thought . It was late when he arrived inside the big house. It was 3:00 in the morning, and Madam was asleep. He was relieved because he was tired and had to get some rest for Emily's so-called wedding, which was to take place in a few hours. He would run the show. He wanted to be well-rested for another night like the one he'd just had with her.

3

Morning came quickly, and it was time to prepare for Emily's so-called wedding. It was set for noon and it was already 9:00 in the morning.

Madam felt a little guilty about the night before, so she turned over in bed to kiss her husband, but he was still asleep. That didn't stop her from reaching down under the sheets and touching him all over. He must have been dreaming about Emily, which broadened the smile on his face while she stroked him. Seeing him smiling like that, she felt hot and ready for him.

"This has never happened between us before," she thought.

Still sleeping, he began to get aroused as she continued stroking him, until he was extended. She took advantage of him, and made love to him while he was still drowsy.

"Oh Emily, it's so good," he called out, enjoying the feeling. He started kissing her, dreaming of making love to Emily. Powerfully aroused, he put his arms around his wife, turned over, and began to make passionate love.

"Oh! Baby, this is so good," he groaned, still asleep. When he began climaxing, he kissed his wife as though she was Emily, and he had never kissed her this way before.

When he awakened he looked for Emily - and came face to face with his wife, who was lying under his body.

"My master plan is all over now," he thought. He didn't know what to do or say.

Madam was feeling really good, never mind that he had called her "Emily." There she was, smiling at him.

"I was dreaming of making love to Emily, but it turned out to be a nightmare," he thought. "What did I say to you while we were making love, dear," he asked sheepishly.

"You said good things to me. Things I've never heard you say before," she replied. "I thought you were trying to apologize to me for the way you acted at Emily's party."

That night she might have conceived her first child. When they got out of bed that Saturday morning, it was after 11:00 a.m, and the so-called wedding was to take place at noon.

Sometimes Master would give the slaves free time when there was a special occasion like Emily's wedding. He set up this event on his plantation for only his slaves to attend. Though he said the celebration was only for slaves, he intended to be there. Madam still wanted to attend this wedding.

"She's like my daughter, and I should be by her side on her wedding day," she said.

It was obvious that he was not happy about this.

"You are not going to attend Emily's affair," he said. "You aren't allowed to attend any slave affair, even if it is for your daughter." He reminded her of the white man's law in the South. "White women are not allowed to socialize with the slaves," he said. That had been the white man's rule for many years.

"And by the way, I meant what I said about making some changes around here, Madam. From now on, slaves will be treated like slaves."

He knew she would be hurt if he did not allow her to attend the affair, especially with her thinking it was her wedding day.

"I've decided to do something special for you and Emily after the celebration," he offered. "I was going to surprise you, but I'll tell you now. I've got a picture man coming. You will be able to see the whole wedding in pictures! It will be like you were there the whole time." He knew he was scoring points with her, so he continued.

"Also, I'm going to take you both into town to shop. You can buy her some of those cute little nightgowns. After all, she'll be a new bride."

That made her happy, since she thought that the sexy nightgowns were for Old Harry's eyes.

Old Harry, Emily, Miss Lilly and Willie had all been told different stories, but Master was sure no one would put all the facts together. He gave Miss Lilly a story because she had to play along when she came into the big house to get the food.

When Madam saw Miss Lilly come into the house, she ran into the room after her. She couldn't wait to hear some news.

"How is she feeling? How does she look?" She asked eagerly. Miss Lilly knew that she had to keep everything in order with the master plan. She had to lie.

"Old Harry and Emily look very happy, and they look just fine as can be," she told her. She knew how much she cared for Emily, and that she was hurting since she couldn't attend the wedding. So she went along with Master Hoover and said things to make her feel better.

"Emily looks real pretty," she said. "Madam, you have made a proper lady of her."

The lies were going pretty well, so Miss Lilly decided to decorate them a bit more.

"Madam Charlotte, because of you Emily was looking like a queen today, and they were just the best looking couple this side of the Mississippi!"

"Oh! Miss Lilly, you are an angel from up above! I really needed to know something." She felt much better, thanks to Miss Lilly, but it didn't stop there. Miss Lilly was feeling good about herself, so she started adding even more information to her story.

"Madam Charlotte, you should see the way Old Harry kissed Emily. She held him very close. It was so romantic." I could tell she was enjoying herself, trying to help Madam Charlotte feel better. Just as she was getting ready to make up a few more things, Master Hoover walked in. He had been listening to her lies behind the door the whole time, wanting to see what she would say to Madam when he wasn't around. When she told the lie about the kissing, he put a stop to it. He didn't enjoy thinking about Emily kissing anyone else, and he was afraid she might soon say the wrong thing.

"No one is as good at deceiving people as me," he thought.

"Now Miss Lilly, let's not gossip. That's enough details for Madam." He went on to say, "You get back out there and keep your big eyes open." She stopped talking and ran out back as fast as she could.

"He's gonna get me for talking too much," she thought.

He wasn't angry with her. In fact, he was proud of the way she handled herself.

"Just don't talk so much next time," he told her later. "The trick is, only tell as little as possible."

Dressed in his best suit, Master Hoover watched Emily during the entire affair, looking like he wanted to marry her himself. She wore the beautiful wedding dress that Madam Charlotte bought for her for this occasion. She wanted to make sure that this day was remembered forever. Master Hoover ordered a picture man to take photographs of her and all the slaves on her wedding day. These pictures were for him. He thought this was a good way to fool Madam. He told her that she could put a picture of Emily on the wall in the big house. This pleased her very much, because she wanted to see Emily in her wedding dress badly. He kept his word and had a large picture framed and mounted in the foyer. When Madam wasn't around, he'd study that picture and think private thoughts.

He had a picture of himself with Emily as if he was the groom. I remember a rumor about that picture. He gave it to her, and until her death, no one had ever seen it except her and Master Hoover. She kept it hidden in her private box in the nanny's quarters. She looked at it whenever she felt alone. On her deathbed, she gave the picture to her seventh son, but by then Master Hoover was long gone.

One thing he didn't do was let the picture man take pictures of Old Harry alone with Emily. Old Harry wasn't invited to the celebration at all, but he had been ordered to show up later to drive the carriage to the river. He kept the picture-man waiting until he arrived after the celebration. He did order a photograph taken of Old Harry with Sister Harriet, Pastor Martin, Willie, Miss Lilly, and himself, with Emily.

In his master plan, he intended to honeymoon with Emily by the river, where they would make love under the moonlight. She was expecting a passionate night celebrating their beginning. She felt proud because when Madam Charlotte had taken her to town to pick out her wedding dress she had also bought her a soft white dress to wear on the special first night with her husband.

"This is for Old Harry's eyes only," Madam whispered. This was because the gown was completely sheer. "Don't wear a thing under this dress, to show off your body. That will arouse Old Harry's nature."

Emily planned to wear that dress with the Master to arouse his nature. Master had told Madam Charlotte that he was going to drive the wedding couple to the river for their honeymoon, and wouldn't be back until late that night.

When Old Harry arrived back at Hoover Ranch with the carriage, he hoped to get some sleep because he was very tired. He had been working for Mr. Montgomery the whole day. The moment he got to the ranch Master Hoover gave him a suit and told him to put it on in case Madam was looking out the window. Then he had to pose for some pictures with Emily and other slaves.

"Okay, get to your quarters for some rest. Be ready to go in one hour," he said, finally. Old Harry headed toward his quarters by the barn, very much in need of sleep because he had spent the night with Sweet Anna. It seemed like a short hour when Master showed up at the barn to wake him, pretending that he was planning to chauffeur the newlyweds. His master plan was working from start to finish, and he was pleased.

Well, all these manipulations were just too much for me. I made up my mind to stay out of the way. I kept on telling myself that I was there just to watch. I decided to go with them to the river to see him make love to Emily again. I wanted to see the passionate love affair that was getting ready to make history, because I sensed that somehow it was my own history as well as theirs.

He knew that Madam Charlotte would be watching in the window as they left. After he got Old Harry out of bed and ready to go, Emily came out looking sexy in her soft white dress and nothing else. Besides the sheer dress, she had on only a beautiful wrap around her shoulders.

I noticed that Old Harry still looked sleepy, but when he took one look at Emily, it sure woke him up. As they drove past Madam's window, just as he thought, she was indeed watching. She saw Emily and Old Harry riding inside the carriage and Master Hoover driving the horses.

"Wave to her. Smile, now," he ordered the so-called honeymooners.

He made sure that Emily knew that she was not allowed to talk to Old Harry at any time.

"Don't embarrass him," he advised her. "He won't know what to do if you mention what I told you about his love affair with Sweet Anna."

"Master, I am not going to talk to him about anything because it is embarrassing to me too, seeing that he preferred another woman over me. Why should I talk to him anyway? I'm not promised to him anymore."

He was proud of her and impressed. The master plan was still working.

Madam knew they would be gone late into the next morning. They didn't know it, but as soon as they passed out of view another carriage was coming down the road toward the Hoover Ranch. It was Percy Carson, on his way to visit Madam Charlotte. The head night watchman on the ranch stopped the carriage to see who it was. The masters of the Montgomery and Carson plantations were never stopped at any time, day or night. They were always welcome at each other's homes, without question.

Madam knew it was going to be a long evening all alone.

So, she sent Willie to Percy with a message inviting him to come calling that night. She was also working on her own master plan, which involved increasing the amount of passionate love in her life.

Master Hoover drove his carriage away from the ranch until he thought he was far enough away, when he stopped and told Old Harry to get out and finish driving them to the river. Emily never looked at Old Harry, nor did she speak to him.

Back at the ranch, when Madam saw the carriage coming toward the house she ran down the stairs, out the door, onto the porch and into Percy's arms. They kissed and hugged and went into the house, straight to her bedroom.

Percy had fallen in love with her as a young boy and had never stopped loving her. Tenderly, passionately, they made love to each other for the second time.

In the mean time, the Master and Emily were locked in tender conversation.

"I just don't feel comfortable about Old Harry now that he disrespected you," he said.

"I'll admit that I was very angry with him for not wanting to marry me," Emily admitted. "Sometimes I really want to make him sorry about his choice to be with Sweet Anna."

I do believe she was jealous, and she really believed he told her the truth about Old Harry. She didn't know that he lied to her just like he lied to everyone else, and she didn't realize he prided himself on being "The Master of Deceit." He put his arms around her and they began kissing and holding each other. She was hoping that Old Harry was looking. And he was, until he was told to drive on.

Old Harry was surprised at the way Emily acted toward him. For my part, I really wanted to do something, but I decided not to keep trying to interfere. I kept telling myself, I'm just here to watch.

When Old Harry got to the river he stopped the carriage.

"What a beautiful moonlight tonight!" He commented. Master Hoover just looked at him.

"You just stay here in the carriage and get some sleep.

You're sleepy," he said. Then he took Emily by the hand, and helped her out of the carriage with tender care. Putting his arm around her body he walked her out closer to the river. They found a spot around the bend behind a large rock very near the river. It even had a waterfall. I could tell he was trying to find a place far out of Old Harry's vision.

Safely out of sight, they felt comfortable being romantic with each other. Their honeymoon spot was covered with soft green grass. He carried the same blanket that he used to wrap around Emily the night he brought her to the ranch from the slave auction.

Old Harry was so angry with him that he was tempted to tell Emily what he had done to stop their marriage. He wanted her to know about the master plan. He thought the Master was trying to have his cake and eat it too. But he knew there wasn't anything that he could do, so he just resigned himself to live without Emily. She was never intended for him anyway.

Master Hoover took the blanket and spread it over that soft green grass. As he put down the blanket, Emily slipped her arms around him. She began to touch him all over his chest and between his legs. He was surprised, but thrilled that she was so relaxed and sexual. They continued their passion down on the blanket. The moon danced over their heads as they touched each other and rolled all over the beautiful soft grass carpet. They were filled with hot passionate desire as they wrapped their bodies around each other, kissing each other deeply.

Then she did something that really surprised him. She started kissing him all over his body. She took her soft hands and moved down his body touching him gently, until he was very excited. He was moaning with such acceptance, and she knew he was aroused. So was she.

"Oh, you're marvelous," he said. She kept on kissing him all over his body until he could not wait. They made love late into the night.

He was still amazed at her knowledge of sexuality and tenderness. He loved the way she turned on that burning desire in him; an intensity that he had never known before. He held her in his arms after they made love and looked into her eyes filled with love.

"This is a romantic evening that belongs only to us," he whispered, nibbling her ear.

Then Emily said,

"Master, I wanted to make Old Harry happy by making love to him with my body, my hands, but most of all my heart," she was saying.

"You can forget Old Harry. He belongs to Sweet Anna. You belong to me now, and I want you to be all of that for me. I have loved you from the start," he said.

I watched them kiss again, passionately. I watched them touching all over each other's body again, and I saw them begin to make love all over again. Before they left the river Emily looked into his eyes and said, "I love you."

"I love you too, and I love making love to you with all of my heart," he replied.

He knew then that he had convinced her that it was alright to be lovers. At this point she was enjoying sex with him. The secret of it all made it more desirable to her, and nothing else mattered. Sex was new to her, and she was really enjoying it. She wanted him whenever he wanted her.

"Don't tell Old Harry anything we talked about," he reminded her. "Our love is our secret only. We want Madam Charlotte to think Old Harry fathered all of your babies." In his heart, he really wanted Emily to be his wife, but he realized that was not possible.

Emily knew that she was hooked on him and it looked like he was even more hooked on her. I began to wonder if she would ever learn the truth about him. Somehow I didn't think she wanted to know, or maybe she already knew and didn't care. I noticed them getting ready to leave the river, so I picked myself up from my spot and ran to get in the carriage before anyone else.

I had forgotten that Old Harry was in the carriage sleeping. When I got in the carriage he got up, as though he heard me. They all returned home about 3:00 in the morning and by this time, Master Hoover was very sleepy.

"Carry Emily back to her room Old Harry, and don't wake her up," he said.

He looked up at the window to see if Madam Charlotte was still up. He hoped not, but he was surprised because she certainly was still waiting up for him. There she was looking out the window. He feared that he'd been found out. He never suspected that Percy Carson just left and that was the reason she was still up. She just finished cleaning herself up in a bath and she was hoping that Master would be too sleepy to want sex from her. She was trying to think of a plan that would keep him from wanting her.

"He's had a long day," she thought. But he'd been watching Old Harry and Emily make love, and was sure to come in wanting her. She was distracted for a minute when she saw Old Harry carrying Emily. "How romantic," she thought. Oh! I'd better get in bed! She hurried to her bed and climbed in, pretending she was asleep.

She didn't know that he saw her in the window, so she didn't know that he knew she was still up. He was wishing she was asleep because he didn't want to make love to her either. So he decided to think of something to do for awhile, hoping she'd go to sleep before he made it to the room.

"I guess I'll go with Old Harry," he decided. "He probably needs help getting Emily inside." He accompanied Old Harry until she was settled in and then sent him back to put the horses away.

"See to the horses, then get back to the barn for bed," he instructed. Old Harry was mighty angry at him for taking beautiful Emily from him, but what could he do?

When Master got to his bedroom, he was surprised and pleased to find his wife asleep. I could tell she was pretending. She knew that he would smell her body, fresh from bathing after being with Percy, and she was hoping that her fresh scent turned her husband on with a sexy feeling because of guilt. So when he got into the bed, she turned over to kiss him. Then she opened her legs all across the bed in a sexy way to let him know that she was ready for him.

"I've been waiting for you sweetheart," she said.

"I'm awfully tired. It was a real long day, with the wedding and all," he said.

She was happy to hear him say that, but she didn't want him to know she was glad.

"I understand," she said. "I'll wait until you feel better. Good night, sweetheart." And with that she turned to go to sleep. With a surprised look on his face, he turned over and went to sleep right away. I was surprised too. I watched her. She seemed happy and content. They were both working a master plan.

4

I was beginning to feel very tired and sleepy. I hadn't been sleepy or even felt tired like this before. Then I heard someone call out my name. I went to the window, but I couldn't see anyone there. I heard it again. It was louder this time. It kept getting louder and louder. I could hear it very clearly.

"Millie," it said. It sounded far away.

I wondered if I was being sent to another place. Then I heard it again.

"M...i...l...l...i...e..." It was getting closer and closer to me.

"Open your eyes," the voice said. I thought my eyes were already open. I started to think I was dreaming, but when I opened my eyes everything was clear to me. I was sitting at my desk in front of my computer. I knew then that I had been on a trip with a spirit. When I looked into my computer I noticed that I had been writing everything as I saw it. I was very frightened. I had written many pages of my imaginary story about slave times, but I didn't remember writing it. I could only remember the trip back in time; it was so fantastic that I could hardly wait to return. I felt the spirit all around me in the room, until I heard voices talking in the house downstairs.

The first thoughts I had were that more spirits were downstairs. Then I remembered my sister and my best friend were visiting. To me it was more like they were visiting with each other because I was upstairs writing my story, and they were downstairs talking.

I jumped up from the computer and ran downstairs to tell them about my dream, but it didn't seem like a dream.

"Girl, you look like you saw a ghost!" My girlfriend was

concerned about me when she saw me. I told her about the spirits.

"You better stop writing for awhile, before you get sick," she said. "You are getting too fascinated with the spirits."

It was too fascinating for me to stop. I had written everything in the computer. I knew that I had to see it through to the finish.

I went upstairs and started to read what I had written, and in no time I was on my journey again. I wasn't asleep, but the spirit was inside me again. I was listening carefully to the voice in my head, which sounded like my Big Daddy. I couldn't see him so I sat down in the chair in Master Hoover's bedroom. I watched him and Madam Charlotte sleeping in their bed. Sitting there in the chair, I fell asleep too.

When I opened my eyes, I felt the presence of my Big Daddy standing over me. I knew he was there to comfort and encourage me not to quit searching for my past. I could feel him and hear him in my heart, but I couldn't see him. I started to wonder if I was really dreaming. At least I thought I was. My eyes started to close again. As my eyes closed, I could feel my hands on the computer keys. The voice was trying to tell me something but I couldn't hear it. I had a sense that time was passing very quickly.

When I opened my eyes I was still in their bedroom, but the Hoovers were no longer in bed. Then I realized that it was not the same. The room looked new. It was set up for a baby. Even the chair was different. I woke up in a pretty white lounge chair, reclining back.

I felt my arm extended out like I was carrying a baby. It really felt like I was holding a baby, but the feeling went away quickly as soon as I saw what had happened while I was asleep. There I was in a baby's room set up for two babies. I wanted to know who was about to give birth.

Lots of baby things were in this room. I noticed there were two baby beds. "Someone must be having twins," I thought. I tried to figure out who it would be.

I heard voices in the hallway coming toward the room. I

was frightened so I ran behind the chair. Soon I realized that they couldn't see me anyway, so I came out from behind the chair and stood there. It was Madam and Emily. "Oh my goodness, they were both very pregnant! But I wasn't gone that long," I thought. This must be like watching a movie; if you don't stay awake you miss a lot. I really missed a lot! I was so happy that I hadn't gone for good. I really wanted to see Emily have her firstborn son, who I knew would be my great-great-grandfather.

When they came into the room they were both talking about the babies' room. Master Hoover was building a new part to his master bedroom for the babies. Now I understand why the room looked different; it was being turned into a nursery for the babies.

They looked like they were ready to give birth any day now. I wanted to talk to them, so I tried.

"When are the babies due to arrive?" I asked. They kept on talking as though they didn't hear me. To my surprise Emily stopped and looked around as though she heard me.

"What's wrong Emily?" Asked Madam.

"I thought I heard someone talking to us," she said.

"I didn't hear anything," said Madam. "What did the voice say?"

"It sounded like a little girl's voice," she said. " The little girl asked when our babies are due." Then they laughed, because they had been talking about names for a girl child. They knew that Master Hoover wanted boys.

"Old Harry wants a boy also," said Emily. At first I was confused when she said that. "Oh, I see," I thought. She is still playing that game with Madam Charlotte. She was keeping the secret about who the child's father really was. Maybe Madam's child's real father was also a secret.

Emily wanted a boy, but she didn't want her to know that. She wanted a lot of children; and all boys. She was afraid of having girls. She feared that they would take the girls away from her, or they would be used as bed warmers for some other slave owner. Since she had been taken away from her own mother, she didn't want that to happen to her child.

I heard them say the babies were only a month apart. If that were true, it would mean close to a year had passed already! I couldn't believe it. I'd only taken a nap for a few minutes. I wasn't about to take any more naps because I didn't want to miss any more; not when babies were about to be born!

"I hear Master coming, Madam," said Emily. He was getting home from a business trip.

"We must get ready for dinner. It must be time if he's home. Let's go check with Miss Lilly," said Madam.

They left the room and walked right into him.

I noticed that one thing had not changed at all; the way he looked at Emily, even being pregnant. She looked at him with passion also. She was eight months pregnant, and looked as though it was time to go down to give birth any day.

Madam looked even bigger, but they told her that she was only seven months along. If that were true, it looked to be a large baby.

"Miss Lilly's calling for dinner," Master Hoover said.

I ran out into the kitchen to see her and saw that she was having a baby also.

She was as big as the others were. "There will be lots of children running around this place soon," I said to myself. They were all going to give birth around the same time.

I noticed how Madam looked at Master Hoover when he entered the room. She was watching him as he looked at Emily. She reached out and hugged him. I knew that she was just showing off in front of Emily. She noticed her husband's reluctance to hug her.

"Don't be shy in front of Emily," she said. She was noticing something.

However, all of her passionate looks at him were just for show, because she was still in love with Percy. He tried to get her to leave her husband and move to Chicago with him.

"Oh, Percy, I can't leave my family here in Mississippi," she had said. She also knew that she was often ill and was unable to take care of a baby without Emily's help. Madam would need to take her with her if she left, but she would never leave Master Hoover anyway.

Percy loved her a lot because he changed his mind about Chicago and stayed in Mississippi, just to be near her.

"I've lived most of my life without you already," he said. "Now that we have found each other again, I'm not about to let you go. I'll take you any way that I can get you, even if it has to be a secret forever!"

Emily had moved into the nanny's quarters inside the big house, since she was going to start breast-feeding the babies as soon as they were born. Madam and Emily acted just like mother and daughter. They were having fun going over baby things and getting ready for the little bundles of joy to arrive.

I was surprised when I saw how big Miss Lilly had gotten. She was carrying Master Montgomery's child, from the night Mr. Montgomery took her as his bed warmer.

Later that night, Emily left the big house and went for a walk around the ranch alone. After she had her dinner alone in the nanny's quarters, she felt depressed. Although she was supposed to be part of the family, at times she did eat her dinner alone in her room. Sometimes Master Hoover would go to keep her company for a while and they would make love. This night he didn't, so she went for a walk.

Madam Charlotte looked out the window and saw her walking around the ranch alone. She called Master Hoover.

"Where is Old Harry? I don't want Emily walking around this big ranch alone at night in her condition."

"I'll go look for him," said Master Hoover. He knew that Old Harry was no longer around Hoover Ranch because he'd gotten rid of him. He didn't really trust him around Emily.

He had traded Old Harry to Master Montgomery for a favor, but Madam still didn't know about it. Now Old Harry could only come to Hoover Ranch to make deliveries. She saw him coming and going and would keep believing he fathered Emily's babies. I was amazed at the way the Master controlled people's lives. During these trips to the past, I discovered the deceitful side of my family and I didn't like it.

Sweet Anna and Old Harry were falling in love since they were together all the time. They had a child on the way. Since he was there most of the time, he decided to act like he was Sweet Anna's husband. She loved him too.

Master Hoover left the house quickly to go see about Emily. When he caught up with her, she was surprised to see him. He wanted to kiss her badly, but knew Madam Charlotte was watching from the window. He also knew that she couldn't hear what they were saying to each other so they talked.

"I want to take you in my arms and hold you forever," he said. "Madam Charlotte is watching so we have to find another moment."

To her, it seemed that they were talking about Old Harry. She'd been afraid that Emily might get hurt walking alone at night during this time in her pregnancy. Reassured to see Master Hoover walking with her now, she turned and walked away from the window.

I went along with them as they walked. I didn't want to miss anything in their relationship.

"I've missed you terribly since moving into the main nanny's quarters, but Master, we can't see each other anymore. Not until Madam Charlotte and I have the babies."

She had a sad look on her face.

"But we haven't been together since you moved inside the big house," he said.

She was feeling sexy and so was he.

"Neither of us likes the separation, but there's nothing we can do about it," she said.

As he walked with her, he started thinking about the way Madam Charlotte came into his life.

"What's on your mind?" Emily asked.

"I was just thinking about times when I was younger," he said.

"Tell me," she urged.

"Well I met this girl in Chicago when I was in college. She was the most beautiful girl that I had ever seen. I fell in love with her and wanted to marry her, but she was not a white girl. She was one-third colored. She looked white, but she never denied the fact that she was colored." He stopped walking and looked at Emily.

"You remind me a lot of that girl, and how much I once loved her."

"What happened? Why didn't you marry her?" She asked.

"I wanted her to tell my father that she was a white girl, but she wouldn't tell a lie, even for me." He choked up suddenly at the memory of losing his first love. Emily noticed the tears that were rolling down his face. He went on.

"Emily, she said to me, 'I wouldn't tell a lie like that to anyone!' And after that I felt her slip away from me like running water."

"Why didn't you just tell the truth?" She asked.

"Well, she had a light-skinned colored mother and a white father. She was beautiful inside and outside, just like you, Emily. So I did tell the truth. I went back home and told my father that I wanted to marry her."

"Good for you," she said.

"But my father said she was just a nigger and he wasn't about to have any nigger blood running through the veins of the Hoover family. Emily, that's why I don't approve of slavery, and why I protect my slaves." He added, "A man should be free, and one day, Emily, that will be so."

When he finished college he came back to Mississippi to take his place as owner of Hoover Ranch.

"How did you meet Madam Charlotte?" She asked.

"My father was paid a large sum of money to arrange a marriage with Charlotte Montgomery. She was my best friend at the time. Our parents were friends, so we ended up together every Sunday," he said.

He looked so sad telling this story to Emily, but I felt as though he needed to tell her to clear his own mind. Somehow I knew he felt it would put his heart at peace.

"One evening, father brought her home. 'This here's your

wife, boy!' he said. The fee had already been paid. I had no choice in the matter. It was to marry her or lose my inheritance." He looked into Emily's eyes.

"So you see Emily, I was never in love with Madam Charlotte. Our marriage was arranged by our parents. Charlotte and I were good friends at that time, and we still are, but she was in love with Percy Carson."

"What happened to the girl in Chicago," asked Emily.

"I thought about that girl for many years," he said. "When I saw you at the slave auction, standing on that stage looking so delicate and pretty, I knew you were the woman I wanted to spend the rest of my life with."

"I'm sorry about how it worked out. But after you got your inheritance, why didn't you go back to Chicago later and marry the girl?"

"I could have done that, but I would have had to give up my inheritance and start another life somewhere else. I knew I couldn't do that. So I chose to keep my stay in bondage with my father's dreams, keep my inheritance and marry my best friend.

"Why did Madam Charlotte's father want to pay someone to marry her?" She asked. She is beautiful now, and must have been lovely as a girl.

"She had poor health, so her father thought no one wanted to marry her. She has a rare blood disease."

"Oh, so that's what causes her to feel tried and weak sometimes," said Emily.

"Yes, and that's why she needs you inside the house when the baby is born. She wants children, but it will be very dangerous for her to have a child. My plans were to wait until we had other doctors see her for another opinion. I was afraid that having a child could cause her to die, but she didn't want to wait.

"I think I got her pregnant the morning after you and I made love the first time. I was dreaming of you, and when I woke up, I had made love to her. I even called out your name, but I think she didn't notice." He didn't know that his friend

Percy was having sex with his wife about the same time.

"Hearing all these stories makes me love Madam Charlotte even more," said Emily. "I don't want to hurt her in any way."

"Then protect our secret forever and she will never know our love for each other," he said.

They started to walk back toward the main house. His wife was standing in the window waiting.

"Don't worry any more. Things will get better soon," he said.

Emily felt better just talking to him. She missed him so much and she really wanted to be with him alone soon, but it was very hard to arrange while she was living inside the big house.

Master Hoover knew that he needed to work out something because he had to keep Emily's mind on him. He never wanted to lose her affection. I could tell that Master Hoover wanted to be with her as much as she wanted to be with him.

"Emily," Master Hoover said. His tone had shifted to a serious one. "You must not walk alone any more. The baby is due any time, and I'm afraid you might get hurt."

"You know," he continued, "I had to send Old Harry away to Mr. Montgomery's Plantation. I'm going to tell you the truth about him; I couldn't stand the thought of him being so close to you when you stayed in your quarters out back of the house late at night." Enough truth. He had to tell her more lies. "Old Harry wasn't happy living here anyway because Sweet Anna had his child on the way and he wanted to be a father."

Emily didn't say a word about that. She just kept on walking back toward the house. They passed by the barn as a mare was giving birth to her foal. Willie was taking care of her. He was considered an animal doctor.

"Willie can help you when your baby is ready to come. Old doctor Pitts taught him all about the birth of horses, so he can deliver babies.

Master Hoover went in the barn to see how the horse was doing. Emily stood by the door waiting. She wanted him to ask her inside the barn and introduce her to Willie. She could tell that he trusted him.

Willie was a big tall handsome dark slave, and extremely smart. He asked her into the barn, and introduced her to Willie. "Willie has been on the Hoover Ranch for over 40 years, you know. He's partial to Miss Lilly."

It didn't matter to Willie that Miss Lilly was pregnant with Mr. Montgomery's child. He loved her. Willie told her that he would be proud to marry her and be a father to her child.

"Now Emily, if you feel a need to walk at night, Willie will walk with you. But you're not allowed to walk alone any more.

Willie took her by the hand. "Hello Miss Emily, pleased to meet you," he said in his kind voice. "I'll take you walking around the ranch any time you want."

Willie lived out back of the barn with Old Harry, but now that Old Harry was no longer around, he stayed there alone. Until Miss Lilly had the baby, though, he was staying with her. Master Hoover was good to Willie because he could trust him. When the horses were sick or having a foal, no one could handle it better than him.

Willie started working with the horses when he was only five years old. Master Hoover's father sold his parents when he was very young. He was only a baby, so other slaves helped raise him. He took to the horses at a young age and Dr. William Pitts noticed that he had a special touch with the animals and found himself growing fond of him. Dr. Pitts taught Willie all about taking care of sick horses and exactly what to do when a mare was having her foal.

By the time Master Hoover and Emily arrived back at the big house, Madam Charlotte was worried.

"Is anything wrong?" Emily asked.

"What took so long for you to return?" Asked Madam.

"We stopped at the barn to watch a new foal being born," said Master Hoover. "Emily wanted to see its birth. And I wanted to see if Willie needed any help." He told Madam

Charlotte some lies about Old Harry. This led into his real plan.

"Emily wants to go back to the nanny's quarters outside the big house so she can see more of Old Harry," he said. "It's late when he gets home in the middle of the night and she misses being with him."

"Well, why does he get to the ranch so late?" Madam Charlotte wanted to know.

"He's got extra work over at Mr. Montgomery's place. I owe Montgomery a favor so I have to let him work there. A deals a deal," he said.

"I'm sorry. I didn't mean to seem angry, but now that I understand what the problem is we'll work something out," said Madam.

"I can come in every morning when the babies are born," offered Emily.

"It sounds like a good idea for you and Old Harry to have your time together in the outside nanny's quarters," Madam Charlotte admitted.

She was afraid of being alone with a small baby.

"You can't stay in the outside quarters when the babies are born," she said.

"Certainly, Madam. You and the babies will need a lot of care," Emily replied.

She knew that when the babies were born she'd need to move into the big house for at least two years.

"But until then, if I can stay in the outside quarters I can be with Old Harry," replied Emily.

She moved out back right away because she was hoping to see Master Hoover that night. He knew that would look suspicious to his wife, so they waited until the following night. The next day, he couldn't wait to tell Madam Charlotte that the HMC Club was having a meeting that he needed to attend.

"I'll be gone most of the night. If you need any help, Willie will be in the guardhouse to take care of you both."

The only problem was that he was not going to any club meeting. This was a night that he planned to see Emily and they would make love late into the night.

Emily was so happy to see him that she kissed and hugged him all night. At about midnight as he was leaving, they heard a loud sound coming from the slave quarters. He rushed to put on his pants and ran out back, leaving Emily behind. When he got there he found that it was Miss Lilly giving birth.

"Master, where is Willie?" Miss Lilly asked.

"Don't worry Lilly, I'll get him!"

Miss Lilly was doing fine, because she had help from some of the other slave women. She had been in labor all day and they'd been by her side. When Master Hoover saw what was going on, he ran to the guardhouse to get Willie. That's when he saw Percy leaving the big house, but he was too excited to pay any attention. He kept on running to get Willie for Miss Lilly.

"Willie, Oh Willie! Miss Lilly is having the baby right now, and you must go to her," said Master Hoover.

He went right away. Master Hoover returned to Emily.

"Miss Lilly is having her baby," he said, out of breath.

"I want to see if I can help," Emily said.

"My darling, in your condition you need to stay in your own quarters and remain calm. Miss Lilly has enough help. You need to stay put, and relax because your own time is very close now," he said.

He started to remember about the night Mr. Montgomery had sex with Miss Lilly; he had sex with Emily for the first time that same night. He thought that was the night Miss Lilly got pregnant. He wasn't sure if Emily got pregnant that same night. If so, he'd impregnated Emily and Madam Charlotte about the same time. He started to get worried about all the babies being born at once. He stayed with Emily until she retired for the night, then kissed her and went back to the big house. He was looking guilty, but Madam Charlotte had a guilty look on her face too. She was all cleaned up, because she had just finished seeing her lover and this was her way of hiding the affair. She wore a big smile.

Master Hoover suddenly remembered that he saw Percy leaving the ranch. That's what he thought. It was late at night, and he couldn't see the gentleman caller's face in the dark. He turned, looked at Madam Charlotte and said,

"Madam, was Percy the man I saw here at the ranch tonight?"

"Yes, it was Percy, he was looking for his brother Clifton. He wanted to know about the HMC meeting."

He suddenly remembered the HMC meeting!

"Had Percy told her there really was no meeting?" He thought.

Madam replied, "I told him you'd already left for the meeting, and the meeting was usually held at his house."

Master Hoover knew she was lying to him, but he was lying to her also. So he lied to her again and told her that the HMC meeting had been moved from the Carson Plantation to the Montgomery Plantation.

"When I got back from the meeting, I heard noise from the slave quarters. It was Miss Lilly having her baby," he said. "It must be close to your time," he worried. He remembered that that night Master Montgomery had impregnated Miss Lilly. The same night he took Emily, and had not made love to each other since.

"Is Percy going to stay around here now that his mother has passed away, and his brother is alone? He asked."

"I didn't ask Percy anything," said Madam Charlotte, and she tried to change the subject.

"Clifton can use some help running the place. I thought Percy was your lover once," he commented.

She didn't say a word. She just walked out of the room.

On May 30, 1814, Miss Lilly had a fine baby girl. She named her Rosa Carson because she planned to marry Willie Carson. Master Hoover went out back to see the baby. He told them they should start planning their wedding; it was time to jump the broom.

When Master Hoover went to see Emily after Miss Lilly's baby was born, they talked about the baby's name and how cute she was. I was impressed with how happy he was about the baby. I was still there, just watching.

One month later, on June 25, 1814 Willie came running in early in the morning, knocking on the door of the big house. Master opened the door.

"It's time," he said excitedly. "Emily's having her baby now. Miss Lilly is with her. She's in labor right now." Just then Willie noticed a surprising thing; Master Hoover wasn't wearing any pants. When he ran into his room to get them, Madam Charlotte woke up from the noise.

"Emily's in labor. Miss Lilly's with her." He got dressed in a hurry and went to the outside nanny's quarters to see her, without Madam.

The baby was born as soon as she saw Master Hoover's face in the doorway. He was a big boy, and it looked like an eight pound baby.

"Beautiful! Just beautiful! He looks like a white baby though, doesn't he?" Master Hoover asked.

Then picked up his firstborn son by his slave lover, just as proud as any father could be. He looked gratefully at Emily, feeling such love that it took his breath away. She wanted to put her arms around him and kiss him. She was so proud of her son that she had tears in her eyes.

"What shall we name him?"

They decided to name their son Clarence Allen, using Emily's surname. The proud father took the baby back to the big house in his arms.

"You did a good job with Emily. I'm proud of my son and all of you," he told Willie and Lilly.

He went on to say, "Watching you work with her was just like watching a real doctor. You're a good man. Now, have her and her things moved into the main nanny's quarters right away. We need her in the house from now on."

He took another look at his son's little face and left.

When Willie brought her things to her quarters, Master Hoover voiced a concern that had been bothering him.

"I think Madam Charlotte is late on her delivery date. I

want you to stay as close as possible to the main house. I was thinking she should have had her baby before Miss Lilly, and surely before Emily. Do you think it's because of her disease?"

Willie said nothing about Percy's coming and going. He continued,

"You need to go fetch Dr. Pitts as soon as possible when the Madam goes into labor."

I was standing there watching. I heard what Master Hoover said to Willie. I wondered why Willie couldn't deliver Madam Charlotte's baby. Then I realized that it was because he was a colored man.

When Master Hoover came back into the big house with the baby in his arms, Madam Charlotte could not wait to hold this baby in her arms. It was her first grandchild. At least, that's the way she felt. She opened the blanket, and saw that pretty face.

She replied, "This child is absolutely the prettiest baby I have ever seen, and it's a boy. Old Harry must be a happy man right now. I want to tell him that he did well by Emily."

Then she asked, "Did he give his son a name yet?"

Master Hoover was not happy about her saying that the baby was Old Harry's son, but he could not say that the baby was his.

"The child's name is Clarence Allen," he said.

Madam Charlotte was surprised and upset with Old Harry. She said indignantly,

"Why didn't he give him his last name?

Then went out to say,

"Clarence Allen Carson should be the boy's name."

"Old Harry never liked the name Carson, so he wanted the child to carry Emily's last name. He said that the name Carson did not bring good memories to him. Did you ever hear him use the name Carson before? No. He's always been just Old Harry, ever since we've known him," said the Master.

That wasn't enough explanation for Madam, so he told her that it was hurtful to Old Harry to think about the pain that his mother received from her master, old man Carson. Old

Harry grew up with a lot of sad stories told to him about his Mama Sara. The truth is, his mother received much pain for many years from both old Master Hoover and old man Carson.

Three weeks later in the middle of the night when Madam Charlotte was asleep, her water broke. She shook Master Hoover awake.

"The baby is coming!"

He ran down the hall right away to Emily's room, but was so excited he forgot to put on his pants. When he ran into the room in his undershorts to tell her about Madam, she was breast-feeding Clarence.

"What a beautiful sight," he thought. He stopped at the door and forgot what he came to tell her just that quick. He was standing there in the doorway looking at Emily with passion on his mind, thinking he needed to make love to her. When he came to himself, he tried to remember what it was that he came into Emily's room for. His mind was on kissing her, and making passionate love to her. She looked up and noticed him standing there without his pants on.

"What do you want?" She asked.

"You have the prettiest breasts that I've ever seen," he stuttered.

She realized that he had been standing there for a few minutes in his undershorts, watching her. She noticed his desire for her. He was getting aroused.

"Master Hoover, is there something that you have to tell me, or do you want something from me?" asked Emily.

He stopped and thought about it. When he came to himself this time he remembered what he wanted.

"Oh my goodness, I am so sorry! Oh Yes! Madam Charlotte is getting ready to have the baby."

Emily jumped up.

"Hurry, go get Willie to fetch the doctor, and tell Miss Lilly to come quickly!" She picked up Clarence and went to her Madam's side right away. She laid Clarence in one of the baby beds that Master Hoover had made for both babies. Clarence was still asleep. Madam Charlotte was in terrible pain. When she saw her she began to relax her. She held out her hands to hold Emily's. She said,

"I'm frightened. I think I may die because of my illness."
Emily replied,

"Now don't you worry. You're going to be all right. I'm going to take good care of you and the baby."

She felt like this was the least that she could do for her Madam.

"You took care of me when I was a young girl, now it's my turn to take care of you," Emily said.

"You still remember how it was when you were young," said Madam Charlotte. She went on to say,

"Emily, I really do believe that you love me, and you are going to take good care of me, but I have something to talk to you about. It has been on my mind for some time now, and I feel that I must tell you now. I have a secret to tell you that I have been carrying around for months now, that I have been wanting to share with you."

I was standing there speechless as she continued speaking her mind to her.

"I think it's time for me to talk to you about this, just in case I don't make it. Master Hoover and I are not in love with each other, and I don't think he is the father of this child that I am carrying. But I cannot tell him this at all. If I did, he would get rid of me. It is true, I have been having an affair with Percy since he returned home."

She asked Emily to keep it a secret unless she died. Then she could do with the secret whatever she wished. I don't think Emily heard anything except that Master Hoover and Madam Charlotte were not in love with each other, and that they never had been. Emily told her that her secret was safe forever. Then she put her arms around her.

"Now relax, so the good Lord will give you peace, and then your baby can come into the world."

Just as Madam Charlotte finished her conversation with her, Master Hoover walked into the room, and he seemed happy to see Emily comforting her.

"I sent Willie to fetch Dr. Pitts."

Miss Lilly came in with clean towels, hot water and all the different oils that Dr. Pitts always used whenever he was delivering a baby. Emily and Miss Lilly cleaned up Madam Charlotte. She was all ready to give birth to her baby when the doctor arrived. Dr. Pitts came in and checked to see how far the baby had moved. The baby's head had dropped into the birth canal. It was time to start pushing.

"Something is wrong," Master Hoover was thinking. This baby is almost a month late.

Dr. Pitts noticed him pacing the floor, and he knew that he was worried, so he told Master Hoover to go outside and wait until the baby was born.

Dr. Pitts knew he was not going to be able to take care of Madam Charlotte unless he got rid of Master Hoover. He had to think of a way to get him out of the way.

"Go wait with Willie," he said. "We'll call you when it's time to look at your new baby." Willie was the doctor's favorite of all the slaves. When Willie's parents were sold off the Hoover plantation, he didn't even have a name. Dr. Pitts really liked him, so he gave the child his first name; William. But they called him Willie. His parents' last name had been Carson, and he kept that last name. Willie was a very smart little boy and liked by everyone, but most of all Dr. Pitts adored him. Whenever he came to the ranch to check on any of the horses, Willie would come running. When a mare was giving birth to her foal, he always wanted to help even as small as he was, at five years old.

Dr. Pitts was ready for the birth, but he was worried about Madam Charlotte. He knew that she might have some real bad complications. Emily and Miss Lilly had already brought in all the things that Dr. Pitts always used whenever he delivered a baby. He always asked for a large bottle of whiskey, hot water, alcohol, peroxide, mineral oil and some clean towels.

It looked like the baby was stuck. They could see the baby's head, but it just wouldn't come out. Emily stood up and grabbed Madam's legs. With Miss Lilly's help, they pulled her legs all the way up over her head, and then they told her to push hard. She pushed as hard as she could. And then it happened - the baby came.

Master Hoover was outside waiting with Willie. He was afraid his wife might die. He remembered what her father had said to him the day they got married. Her father was certain that if she had a baby, she would die in childbirth. Her father told him not to get her pregnant.

He said,

"If you do get her with child, you had better pray, and pray hard. If you want a son you should get one of your half-white slaves to bear him. Then take the boy and raise it as your own and keep your mouth closed."

Seeing the surprise on Master Hoover's face, Madam Charlotte's father grew impatient.

"Boy! Learn to keep secrets, just like your old man did." Old man Hoover was known as "The Master of Deceit," a title that young Master Hoover had always wanted. "No one will know the difference if your bed warmer bears your son. We'll all think it's a white child by Charlotte. You can make it so."

Master Hoover was trying to do just what his father-in-law suggested. He never wanted Madam Charlotte to become pregnant by him. She wanted a child of her own, so she took advantage of a situation one night when she was horny and became pregnant, so we all thought.

Since she was having an affair with Percy, who knows the truth. Not even Master Hoover knew, but I think Madam Charlotte did. Master Hoover was so worried about her that he thought out loud with his head down in his chest.

"I didn't want her to go though this pain, or take any chance of dying." Then he heard the baby crying and that made him happy because he thought everything was all right with Madam Charlotte.

When he went into the room, the doctor told him the bad news.

"Your baby is fine, but Madam Charlotte isn't out of the woods yet," he said. "It's been a long, hard procedure, and we almost lost her."

He stood in the doorway looking at the three of them and noticed Emily holding a blue blanket in her arms. "Come look at your son, and then we can talk about your wife's care and answer any questions that you may have," said Dr. Pitts.

He walked over to look at his new son, and took him from the arms of his lover. As he looked into the face of his second son, he thought about the morning that he thought this son was conceived.

He thought that this baby was born late, perhaps causing Madam Charlotte to have such a hard time giving birth. As he stood, deep in thought, Dr. Pitts called him, trying to get his attention.

"I'm sorry?" He finally heard his name. "I was thinking about a name for my son."

"Madam will need at least three to five weeks of careful care to survive this ordeal," Dr. Pitts said. "She's lost a lot of blood and is still bleeding. I had to use a lot of packing in her vagina, but I haven't entirely stopped the bleeding." He turned to Emily and Miss Lilly.

"You must change the packing every day to keep from setting up any kind of infection."

"Is my wife going to die?" He asked, giving the baby to Emily.

"That is not up to me. I assure you I will do everything in my power to save her, but she faces a long, hard battle," said Dr. Pitts. They all knew it was going to take lots of prayer and hope for Madam Charlotte to survive.

"I'm willing to cooperate in any way that is needed to help Madam Charlotte get well," he said. "She is my best friend, and Dr. Pitts, I would do anything to keep her on this ranch with us. I need to keep her from dying."

I was surprised to hear him refer to Madam Charlotte as his best friend. I was still there watching, but this was one of my sad days. I thought he could be a good person sometimes, but I couldn't believe that at a time like this he could call her his best friend.

"We'll do the best we can." That's all Dr. Pitts would say. The doctor had given Madam Charlotte a large dose of whiskey for her pain, so Master Hoover had no chance to talk with her. He was not happy about that.

Everyone had a job to do to save Madam Charlotte's life. In order to get her well, they had to work together. Emily's job was to take care of the babies. That was fine with her, but she wanted to be near Madam Charlotte too. She brought both of the babies into Madam's room so they could all be near each other. She breast-fed the babies as she watched Madam Charlotte sleep. She also thought that if Madam could hear the babies crying, it might strengthen her will to fight for life.

Master Hoover knew how much Emily loved her. I guess he was trying to be a loving friend, husband or whatever he thought he was to the Madam. I wondered if he did it just so he could keep himself looking good in Emily's eyes.

Miss Lilly's job was to make sure Madam Charlotte had a good meal every day. That was easy for her, since she was the house cook. She had a small baby of her own. Between cooking and breast-feeding her own baby she was exhausted. Every day She made her chicken broth soup. Every day she put the soup in a bottle and laid Madam's head in her lap to feed the soup to her. She was unable to feed herself because she was asleep most of the time, so Miss Lilly fed her like a baby.

Dr. Pitts was a great friend and a fine doctor. He changed her packing everyday, and that kept her from getting infections. The doctor even slept outside her room, day and night.

Three weeks passed with no change in Madam's condition. Master Hoover and Willie were very worried.

"I need to get her well so she can see her beautiful baby," Master Hoover told Willie.

Willie knew that Master Hoover was very worried about Madam so he stayed with him all the time, always very supportive to Master. We all wanted her to see her beautiful son; the child that she had always wanted.

One day, Master Hoover went into Madam's room, and he just stood there looking at her. He called out for Emily to come into the room with him. He wanted to give his son a name but he didn't know if Madam Charlotte had selected a name for him already.

I had noticed Emily outside the closed door talking to Willie. She was asking him to help her think of something to get Madam Charlotte well again. They were wondering about the unbreakable chain prayer, which She thought was the best plan. The unbreakable chain would do what no man could do to help Madam Charlotte get better.

Master Hoover was asked to sign his son's birth record for filing in the town hall of records. So, he had to give his son a name. Emily heard him calling her name. She came into Madam's room hoping that she was better, but she wasn't.

"Do you know if Madam Charlotte has chosen a name?" asked Master Hoover. He tried to pretend that he wanted to see her about naming his son, but she noticed him looking at her with passion in his eyes. When she looked into his eyes she knew that he really wanted her body badly.

No sooner than she entered the room, he reached out his arms to hold her.

"Master Hoover please, let's not do this now. Our Madam Charlotte is ill and this is neither the time nor the place to think about ourselves. I can't think of anything but Madam at this time."

He still wanted more, but he knew that he had no choice but to stop, unless he wanted to lose Emily for good. This would be unbearable, especially since there was already a great possibility that he may be losing Madam Charlotte in death. He changed to a safer subject.

"But did she say anything about naming the baby?"

"Madam Charlotte told me that she liked the name Joel Edward, and she had planned to discuss that name with you soon, but I guess she never got the chance."

"Then it's done. My son will be Joel Edward Hoover. Their son was born on July 25, 1814, just one month after Emily's son Clarence was born.

It was so touching to see how much she loved the woman

that she felt was the only mother that she knew. I believed she would have stopped loving Master Hoover if he did anything to hurt Madam Charlotte.

Four weeks later, and with no improvement in Madam's health, Emily called a meeting. She assembled Dr. Pitts, Willie, Miss Lilly, and Master Hoover.

"It is now four weeks and Madam Charlotte's condition has not improved. She is still very weak. We have got to do something, or we may lose her soon. There is only one more thing that I can think of, and that is an 'Unbreakable Chain Prayer.'"

Colored families did this prayer all over the South when they had serious illness in their homes.

"Emily, tell me how does this believer's prayer work?" asked Master Hoover.

"The whole family will join hands in a circle. Then an appointed family member will lead the prayer to God. That person is called "The Believer." The Believer must be a true believer in God."

Master Hoover took a look around in Madam's room and walked to her bedside. As he watched her, the pain showed in his eyes. Emily was glad to see him thinking about doing the prayer, even if he decided not to do it. As long as she had known him, he had never prayed, or even gone to church. Then Master Hoover looked at everybody in the room, even the babies who were still asleep. He reached down to touch his son gently on his head. He was sleeping by Madam. "What would I need to do?" He asked.

"Master Hoover, you would have to truly believe in the power of God," said Emily quietly.

Let's do it!" He looked around the room again.

"I want Emily to be The Believer," he said. What Master Hoover didn't know was that all the other slaves out back on the plantation were joining hands with all of them and lifting up Emily's prayer.

One by one, the people in the room and the slaves on the Hoover Ranch joined hands.

"You all must listen to me very carefully! No matter what happens, don't let go of any hands, until the prayer is completed," Emily paused, because the next instruction was very important. "The circle must not be broken by anyone." Then Emily closed her eyes and began to pray.

My Dear Divine Father, here we all are
coming into your heavenly home, knocking
on your door, with a joint prayer from all of us.
We are asking you to help us please.
I don't think we even deserve a favor from you,
but we are asking you anyway.
We know that you are a forgiving God.
We are all asking for your forgiveness
in our wrong doing, my Lord.
We are not coming to you totally for ourselves today,
but we are asking for Madam Charlotte.
She has not sinned as we have, so please,
Lord, don't let her die.
If it is your will, dear Lord,
to take Madam Charlotte home with you at this time,
then we accept it fully and completely without question.
But Lord, what we have done under your sight,
we know it was wrong, so please, dear God,
forgive us and make us better.
We are a family and we love each other.
We come to you asking you to find consolation
in your power to give Madam Charlotte back
to her newborn son, and us.
We are asking you, Lord, if it's your will.
We love you Lord.
Amen!"

At the end of the Believer's Prayer, everyone held hands for a moment. Then they heard a voice.

"Where is my baby?"

They all turned around. It was Madam Charlotte, sitting up in her bed. In a miracle she was talking and smiling again!

She reached her arms out for her child.

"Thank you for taking good care of me and my baby," she said to Emily. As soon as she could, Emily went out back to thank the slaves for their prayers, telling them that Madam Charlotte would be all right now. That made them happy and they started celebrating by singing with Sister Harriet who was leading a very beautiful old gospel hymn right outside of Madam Charlotte's window.

In spite of the slave's' loud songs of celebration, the babies' slept. The singing lifted everyone's spirits and put them to sleep at the same time. When they noticed that they relaxed to the singing, Emily and Madam Charlotte asked Sister Harriet to sing outside the window every night.

Dr. Pitts was amazed at the way Madam Charlotte came out of her illness. When he finished his examination he said, "It is a miracle!" He told everyone that she was out of the woods and back to her old self again. Master Hoover decided to throw a big celebration party, inviting all of their friends. He also planned to give a party out back for all of the slaves, as soon as Madam Charlotte was on her feet and feeling stronger.

5

For the next two weeks, they kept Madam Charlotte in bed because the doctor said that she needed to build up her strength. When Master Hoover heard that Madam Charlotte was going to be bedridden it was very disappointing to him.

He started to plan her part. He was already planning to spend some of his evenings with Emily having sex late into the night. Emily wasn't thinking of sex. She had planned to spend lots of time in Madam's room, catching up on news and playing with their babies.

"Tell me everything I missed during the last few weeks," Madam urged.

Emily replied, "Master Hoover was dreadfully worried. So was the doctor, Willie, Miss Lilly, Master Hoover, and all the slaves on the plantation. They all joined in the Believers Prayer."

"I had a dream during my illness. I was looking at all of you from a high place, it seemed. It was like looking at everyone in a mirror. I heard you calling me back, but I didn't want to come, until I saw the face of my son." Madam Charlotte told how she was not able to speak during her illness, but she could hear everything around her.

Emily thought perhaps the doctor had over-medicated her, thinking the pain would be too much for her to handle.

Then Madam Charlotte thought about the secret that she told before the birth of her son; the one about Percy Carson.

"Did you tell anyone about the secret?" she asked.

This upset Emily, because she had forgotten about the secret.

"What was it about Madam? I've forgotten it and I am sorry for forgetting. I had so much on my mind that it was impossible to remember all of the things I was told, with you so sick."

"Was it so bad?" asked Madam.

"I was busy with feeding the babies, trying to eat the right foods to have enough milk for both of them, and worrying about losing you."

She wanted to make sure Emily had forgotten what she told her about Percy.

"Madam, I would never want to forget anything you told me." She felt awful about forgetting something so important.

Relieved, Madam Charlotte said, "Oh don't you worry about that because it wasn't important anyway."

"It must be a sign of aging," Emily said, although she was only 21 years old.

Two days later, she was just finishing up feeding both boys and putting them down for the night. She wanted to stay near Madam so both boys slept in her room. They were spending a lot of time together and Master Hoover was starting to feel replaced. This was not making him happy, so one night he decided to go out on the town.

"I'm going to my friend's plantation for the HMC meeting," he told the two women. They were having one of those "First Climaxing" games with the slaves and that usually lasted all night. He wanted to go because he was not getting any attention from Emily or Madam. As he left for the meeting, he thought he was going to have some big fun that night, but when he got there all he could think about was Emily. Watching the sex game with the slave couples from the fields didn't do him any good. When the sex game started, he wanted her even more. He was thinking about getting up and going home, but he thought she would be busy with Madam.

Emily and Madam Charlotte had been talking and playing with the boys all day and night. Emily was finally very tired and so was Madam Charlotte because she fell asleep while Emily was talking to her. She got up and checked on both of the babies and found them both asleep. It was good that they were asleep because she was very sleepy herself.

She noticed that she was the only one awake so she decided to go to her quarters to freshen up. She wanted to get some sleep herself, but first she looked at the babies' again. She took a bath in her washroom and put on one of her sexy nightgowns. She felt sexual after finishing her bath but she was thinking that Master Hoover was out for the evening. So she decided to make love to herself because it had been a long time since she had sex. Just as she got in the bed and opened her legs to masturbate, her door opened, but she didn't hear it. She continued touching herself to the point of almost climaxing. She then heard a groaning sound coming from the corner of her room. She opened her eyes and looked across the room near the door. There was Master Hoover standing in the dark corner touching himself while he watched her. When he noticed that she saw him, he walked closer to her bed wanting her badly.

She opened her arms to him and he went into them so gently that their bodies might have been two magnets, the way that they linked together. He wrapped his lips around her soft tender lips, turning on a body fire like a hot sauna. His body began to sweat as she rolled over pressing her breasts into him and looking into his eyes with such sensuality. They melted into each other with a burning need. It caused an intense, emotionally compelling and electrifying climax, ending with a gentle feeling of acceptance.

This was a night of great love for them. He held her in his arms and kissed her all night. This was the first time they had actually spent the whole night together. The next morning they looked out into the daylight together in bed.

He said drowsily,

"I love you,"

Emily was pleased as she looked into his eyes.

She said, "You are my world my love, but now I have to leave for work." They kissed each other.

She went into the changing room where the water pan and bath towels were and began to wash herself. He was watching her clean her body and soon found himself wanting more of her. He was getting aroused watching her. By the time she came out ready to go to work, he wanted her again badly.

She wore a pretty white cotton dress that he could see the shape of her body through. He couldn't stop himself. Before he knew it he had reached out and grabbed her, pulling her close, letting her feel him fully extended. His nature started to rise until he couldn't wait. He wanted to have her right then.

Suddenly, she heard Miss Lilly outside her door calling for her and they had to stop. She started laughing when she looked at his face because it showed so much disappointment. She went to the door and Miss Lilly was standing there.

"Madam Charlotte is awake and asking for you," she said.

"I'll be there soon, I'm almost dressed."

Miss Lilly went back and told Madam Charlotte that Emily had overslept and was on her way.

"Miss Lilly, I thought Emily was spending the night in my room last night." Madam Charlotte said.

Madam thought since Master Hoover was gone all night with his gambling friends, Emily would stay with her and the children.

"When I woke up and missed Emily, I started looking for her, even though the babies were still asleep. Do you know where she went?" She asked.

Emily got ready to leave Master Hoover, looking back at him and smiling.

"There's some cold water in the bath that might cool you off. I will see you later."

Then she walked out the door.

He laughed at her, sat on her bed, picked up her pillow and held it close to his body. He could smell her on the pillow and he began to hold the pillow as if he was holding her in his arms tenderly. He let his mind wander until he saw Emily's body come back through the door and into his arms again. Soon they were making love in his mind, just like they did last night together. While he was all into his sexual encounter the door opened, and it was Emily. He was almost climaxing and she watched him for a moment, then quietly opened the door, stepped out, and closed it behind her.

Emily stood outside the door and she began to think about that electrifying sexual moment herself. When she came to herself she was caught up in the moment of his passion.

She whispered, and walked away,

"Good day my love,"

She went into Madam's room and the boys were still asleep. Madam was wide awake and very happy indeed to see Emily.

"I missed you. Did you forget Master Hoover was going to be out all night?" Madam asked.

Just as she was getting ready to answer, he walked in. He gave a fatherly pat to the babies' heads. He left to take a bath and changed for a business meeting with the Plantation Association Group. This was an organization started by the plantation owners. During the P.A.G. meetings they discussed the laws of slavery. They talked about the price of slaves, trading of slaves, and war that was getting ready to put an end to slavery.

Suddenly time started to pass fast. As time went on, Master Hoover told his son,

"You can only play with Emily's boy, not the other slave children."

Joel Edward thought Emily was his father's sister, one of the first lies that Master Hoover told him. What did it matter? Joel loved Emily. He thought her son was his cousin.

Names from my present were mixing in with names that popped into my head during my trip to the past. In this out-of-body experience, I was looking at Clarence. Later I would investigate whether there really was a Clarence Allen back in the 1800s, but for now I wrote what came into my head.

Clarence was Emily's first son, born in 1814. Her second son, Willie Leroy, was born in 1815. By now he was four years old. He was named after Miss Lilly's husband Willie. Miss Lilly had become Emily's best friend.

David Roy, her third son born in 1816, was now three years old. Her fourth son, Peter Joe, was also born in 1816.

David was born in January, and Peter was born in December. Peter Joe was almost three. One cute little boy played alone. He looked like he was only one-year-old. This was Emily's fifth son, Evan Lee, born in 1817.

I looked over by the big house and saw a baby in Madam Charlotte's arms. He was Emily's sixth son, Joey Jon, born in 1818. He was born on the birthday of Madam Charlotte's only son, so, Madam named this child. As I watched, Madam Charlotte turned to take the baby inside.

Since Clarence was the oldest, Master Hoover told him that he was responsible for the others, even his son, Joel Edward. He was responsible for something else too; whenever Master Hoover wanted to have sex with Emily, he sent Clarence out back near the barn to watch all of his brothers, so he wouldn't be interrupted.

Master Hoover was 55 years old by this time, and Emily was only 25. She still excited him because of her beauty and youth. I remember thinking men are very strange sometimes because Madam was only 45 years old. She too was a very beautiful lady. Maybe it was true that they'd never been in love. One thing was certain; when it came to Emily, he was head over heels.

I was sad when Dr. Pitts told Master and Madam they couldn't have any more children after the birth of Joel Edward. But it was probably for the best.

Dr. Pitts said firmly, "If you ever get pregnant again you would surely die in childbirth."

They weren't surprised, but she still wanted more children with Master Hoover. He'd had enough of the whole business with her, and didn't want to father any more children with her. On the other hand, he was concerned about having only one son carry the Hoover name into the future. What if this son had only daughters? The Hoover name would be no more.

Emily was giving him one son after the next, but they were Allens, so he started working on a plan. He thought about what old man Montgomery said,

"Have children with a mulatto slave girl and raise them as

your own white children."

This was beginning to sound like a good idea.

Even though she had hoped for more children, Madam Charlotte felt blessed with her one son. She knew that she could have met death during the birth of any child. Of course, she also thought of the family name going into the future. She loved playing grandmother to Emily's sons.

Madam often thought what kind of a father Old Harry was turning out to be. She wondered why he wasn't spending more time with the boys. She didn't know he was living with Sweet Anna, and that she was pregnant with his fourth child. Master told all the slaves that Old Harry was living with another woman on the Montgomery Plantation. He ordered them not to speak of it to Madam. The Master of Deceit always gave a reason that sounded good. He told the slaves not to tell her anything because she was so fond of Old Harry.

Madam thought that Old Harry was still working for the Montgomery Plantation during the day. He came home at night, and every year he was getting Emily pregnant. She thought for a long time that something was wrong with the story, but she was so busy with her love affair that she didn't pay close attention.

One day Madam noticed. When around Master Hoover, Emily was acting like a woman in love. She certainly wasn't acting like he was her father. Around him, she always smelled like a flower, and wore nice sexy dresses. What really made Madam wonder was that she never seemed to be around Old Harry, and didn't even speak to him when he was there.

Then there was Master Hoover. Madam Charlotte knew something was wrong with that picture, and thought for a long time that it just didn't feel right. She'd been secretly seeing Percy for almost six years, and Master Hoover seemed happy all the time.

"Aha!" She thought to herself.

"Old Harry isn't the father of Emily's children because he isn't around the ranch enough to get her pregnant."

She knew this wasn't like the Old Harry that she remembered. Then she remembered that Emily had moved inside the big house when her sixth child was born. Master would never let Old Harry inside the big house to be with her in bed.

"Oh, who am I trying to fool," Madam admitted to herself. "I have known about my husband's love for her ever since the day he brought her here. I just didn't want to believe it. Besides, I needed her myself since I didn't have Percy and didn't love Master Hoover. Raising her as a daughter filled my empty life."

Because her affair with Percy kept Madam happy, she really didn't care.

She thought,

"One day they'll know I was never fooled by their affair. Master Hoover, I am the master of deceit. I know about you, but you don't know about me."

When she figured it all out, Madam Charlotte had them all fooled. She didn't let on that she knew for many more years. Even Master Hoover thought she didn't know what was going on around her. The truth was, she knew everything, but she accepted it.

Madam recalled the day of the Unbreakable Chain Prayer. They thought she couldn't hear, but she was just drunk from all the whiskey the doctor had given her for pain. Now, six years later, it all came back to her.

Madam thought,

"Emily was the believer who led the prayer for me when I was sick. They all thought I was asleep. Well I wasn't. I could hear everything, even Emily's confession that she made to God for having an affair with Master."

It took Madam six years to decipher what was going on around her during that time. Recollections came back to her about Emily and Master talking in her room one day.

"Madam Charlotte means more to me than having sex with you," she was saying.

Madam knew of her husband's affair with Emily, but she didn't know that Emily remembered her confession about Percy during the birth of her son. Even though she felt making love to Master Hoover was wrong, she could not stop. The confession gave her some comfort.

Madam found out about many of the lies that had been told to her over the years. She knew her health was fragile. She thought if she said anything it could cause lot of trouble with Master. She didn't want to be without Emily and the boys.

Madam knew she could live with Percy her lover, or her brother Frederick. Neither was young enough to take care of her when she got old and weak. There were two things she realized she could count on, Emily's love, and the love of her only son Joel Edward. But only Emily would be there all her life to care for her.

Since this was a day of remembering, Madam started to think about her father. She'd heard him, years ago, talking to old man Hoover in the barn. She heard her father tell old man Hoover that he'd saved up over $10,000 to give to him.

He said, "I've saved all this money over the last five years to buy my little Charlotte a life. Now if you would arrange the marriage between your only son and my only little girl, this money is all yours."

"It's not like they don't know each other," said old Man Hoover. They've been good friends all their lives."

He thought a bit. "My good friend, what about your girl's health? And Montgomery, what about the boy your girl is dating, old William Carson's son?"

"True, she is a sickly little thing, but my Charlotte is a fine looking woman. He may be able to get one child out of her, but then again the doctor did say she shouldn't get pregnant because of her blood disease," he said.

Mr. Montgomery had to think a bit to come up with an answer for the first question, but the second answer came instinctively.

"And Hoover, you know I'd as soon as die before I let my only daughter marry in that old rat's family."

Listening to them describe her frailties, and the boy she loved, had been painful for Charlotte. Percy Carson's father wasn't going to arrange for her to marry his son either, because he didn't like Mr. Montgomery any more than Montgomery liked him. She knew she'd never change their minds. Edward Dennis Hoover was her best friend, anyway.

She asked herself, "How bad can it be? I'll be married to a good-looking man like Edward Hoover. He'll be rich, too. All the girls in town wanted him, so better her than them. I can make him fall in love with me after our marriage."

She hoped she would learn to love him too.

Master didn't know what his father had done until the marriage was arranged. Madam wasn't going to be the one to tell him. She kept the conversation she heard in the barn a secret. His father told him that he couldn't marry the half-white colored girl from Chicago. If he disobeyed, he would be disinherited. If he couldn't have the woman he loved, he wouldn't care about a wife. He would do whatever his father told him to do in order to keep his inheritance.

He decided, "Somewhere down the line I'll have a bed warmer and I'll choose a light-skinned colored girl, even if I have to cheat on my wife."

He was determined to be happy, but he hadn't planned on falling in love with a bed warmer. If he had to be in an arranged marriage, he was glad it was with his best friend. Although he tried to learn to be her lover, it wasn't enough.

So her marriage had been full of lies from Master, but she couldn't get angry. Actually she was happy. She would have known all along that Master Hoover would have someone else.

She thought, "Why not Emily?"

He now loved a woman that cared even more about her. It kept him home most of the time. In his mind, Emily is the girl in Chicago. He'll never leave me, and neither will she. In a way she was winning. She thought she was playing the same game as Master Hoover.

One day, far in the future, Madam planned to tell Emily that she had always known about Master fathering her sons. Before Emily, Madam didn't feel that her life mattered to anyone. When she became her daughter everything changed. She had six sons who were now part of Madam's life. Whenever she felt lonely she would call all the boys into the house and play games with them. She taught them how to read. Right along with Master, Madam was planning the future for their grandsons. They were making plans to ensure the children's survival after slavery was over. They filed documents in the hall of records stating the boys were white. The ultimate secret. After that, it was up to them to continue living on the ranch and keep their secrets.

Other states had already freed their slaves. Even though all of Emily's sons were kept a secret from the world, and they could pass for white, the Hoovers felt there was still some risk for them.

Master loved his boys, and he treated them like they were white. He thought Madam was proud of the way he treated the boys. He hoped that Madam thought he was acting like a proud grandfather. He still thought he had her fooled.

They never allowed the boys off the plantation for any reason. They brought everything they needed to the plantation. They only played with children on the Hoover Ranch. When the Hoovers had parties and when visitors came to the plantation, the boys were taken out of sight.

The guards were instructed to keep them from being seen, so they hid the boys. When they grew up, the boys had a choice to pass for white, or to acknowledge their colored heritage. Only Dr. Pitts, the slaves, and close friends who were slave owners themselves, knew the boys even existed. People in town thought the Hoovers were private people because the ranch was built in a way to keep their private life secret.

There were rumors about a newspaperman in town. Someone said that the newspaperman captured a slave named Willie from Hoover's Ranch for information. Willie had been in town running an errand for old man Hoover Sr. When the old man found out he was furious that the owner of the newspaper had tortured Willie. Rumor had it, the slave made it back to the ranch beaten close to death. He was able to tell old man Hoover who had hurt him. The man who Hoover knew was the owner of the Morning Sun Newspaper.

"What did he want to know from you?" Old man Hoover asked.

"Master, all about what went on inside the walls of the Hoover Ranch. That's what he asked about," answered Willie.

The newspaperman and his violent friend thought Willie was dead. They rolled his body down by the river when they were through with him. Old Man Hoover went to see the owner of the newspaper.

"If you write one word, you say anything about my family in your paper, or you ever put your hands on any slave of mine again, then you won't live to read your own paper the next day," said the angry Old man Hoover.

The newspaperman did indeed write a story the next day. He led right off with:

```
Master  Edward  D.  Hoover  Sr.,  owner  of
the   Hoover   Ranch   Plantation,   is   a
deceitful  man.  He  has  built  a  prison  of
secrets  behind  that  brick  wall  he  calls
a  home.
```

The article went on to say:

```
Secrets  are  being  kept  by  everybody,
even  the  slaves,  and  there  may  well  be
some  illegal  business  going  on  behind
those  big  tall  gates.  Old  Man  Hoover
threatened  to  kill  this  newspaperman  if
he  wrote  anything  in  his  paper  about
his   family   or   his   slaves.   In   this
reporter's   opinion,   he   is   a   nigger
lover.
```

The next day the newspaperman didn't show up for work. A copy of the paper sat on his desk unread. Just like old man Hoover said, he never got a chance to read his own article. He never showed up for work again, and he was never found.

The Hoover's never had any trouble after that. No one tried to get through the walls of the Hoover Ranch Plantation or tell any of their secrets. No one knew anything about the Hoover family tree except the Hoovers themselves. After the newspaperman disappeared people seemed to feel a lot less curious. The slaves knew better than to speak of any family business. They were told if they opened their mouths, they would be killed on the spot by the guards, on orders from Old Man Hoover.

I was feeling sleepy again and somehow I felt that if I didn't fight it off, my heart might stop beating at home. If I went to sleep I knew I'd go back to the future. Just as I drifted off, I was awakened by another noise.

It was 1820. I heard a lot of noise in the nanny's house out back where Emily lived. It was Emily and Master Hoover making love to each other. The children were just outside the door playing. I saw Emily's firstborn son, Clarence, taking the boys away as soon as he heard the groaning.

He headed for the barn to spend time with Willie, who was tending to the horses.

I saw Willie and Miss Lilly and I was happy to see them. It looked like they were married; at least they were living together. Then I saw a very beautiful white girl standing in Miss Lilly's door. She was looking out at Clarence. I could tell that she liked him by the way that she watched him. When the boys went over to the barn where the horses were she came running out of the house to Willie who was putting a shoe on one of the horses.

"Father what are you doing?" She said.

I was surprised because she couldn't be Willie's daughter.

Willie looked down at her and said,

"Rosa how many times have you seen me do this?"

She laughed.

"I know, father, but tell me anyway!"

Willie saw Clarence Allen with all of his brothers and he said,

"Oh, Rosa not this again! Why don't you just tell Clarence that you like him?" He said.

Rosa looked at her father, and said,

"Father, that wouldn't be lady like!"

"Okay, I will do it for you," said Willie.

Rosa started laughing because she didn't believe him.

Looking out the barn door at the boys, Willie realized that Master Hoover was having his way with Emily. He went out and talked to Clarence.

"Do you boys want to come in the barn and watch me put a shoe on the horse?"

They were excited about watching, especially Evan Lee. He really loved the horses from the first time he saw them, even though he was barely three years old. Master spent a lot of time showing off his sons to the slaves and teaching them about the horses. The boys went inside with Willie. Clarence knew that it was going to take Master Hoover a while to complete his grown-up game with Emily, like all the other times.

Clarence was six years old, but he was a very old acting six-year-old. Madam used to say that he was beyond his years. This was the day he got to know Rosa. She was already interested in him. As time went by they got to be very good friends, to the point that when they grew up, they got married.

Master and Emily were still having sex in the nanny's quarters when Madam came out of the big house onto the porch. She was looking for the boys, afraid they had wandered off. They were in the barn with Willie. Rosa saw Madam standing out on the porch.

"Clarence, I think your grandmother is looking for you," she said. He walked out of the barn and looked across the way.

"Grandmother are you looking for us?" He asked in a loud voice.

"You boys come on up to the porch," she called back.

Clarence went into the barn to get his brothers to take them home. Madam wanted to tell them that Joel was home from school and ready to play with Clarence, as they did every day after school.

Joel went to school in town because he was white. The guards took him to town to school and they brought him back every day after school.

I thought Madam could hear Master and Emily having sex in the nanny's quarters. When she looked out toward the nanny's quarters as she was calling the boys, but she didn't say anything.

After she got the boys in the house, she played with the smaller boys while Joel and Clarence played together.

6

I found myself falling off to sleep again. It seemed like I was getting sleepy all the time. This time when I woke up I heard something that sounded like crying.

I opened my eyes as quickly as I could.

"Oh my goodness, it's Emily! It looks like she's pregnant again," I thought.

I could tell it was late at night. I saw Master trying to have sex with this very pregnant woman. Then I thought,

"This must be her last child, because she had six sons already."

I couldn't believe that Master was having sex with her, in her ninth month. I looked again.

"Oh my goodness, it looked like her water broke! He thought she was still climaxing with him, but she was crying. Soon he figured it out. She was crying because of the pain from the contractions. The baby was coming. He didn't know what to do, so he held her in his arms trying to comfort her. I wanted to help, so I ran over to Miss Lilly's quarters and tried to wake her. I just walked through walls. I couldn't make any noise. I tried to wake Willie, but with no luck there either. I found myself getting anxious. I ran over to the big house to try to wake Madam. I was surprised that she heard me fall through the door. I felt the door move through my body, and saw Madam jump up like she heard me. That's when she noticed Master wasn't in bed next to her.

She went to the window and looked out and heard crying. After finding her robe and slippers, she threw them on while running out the door to Willie's quarters. This time he heard the knock on his door.

"Willie you must come now. I think Emily is having the baby and there may be problems, so come quickly!"

This was the first time I noticed Madam going out back to the slave quarters. I wondered why she didn't go to the nanny's quarters first, then I realized that she knew Master was trying to have sex with Emily.

She didn't want him to know that she had always known what was going on. She wanted to give him enough time to put on his pants. After she fetched Willie, she went to Emily's door and knocked. He had gotten his clothes on by that time. The boys were awake from all the noise. Madam wanted to get rid of Master, to be alone with Emily.

"Edward, please take the children to Pastor Martin's and see what's taking Willie and Miss Lilly so long to get here," she commended.

As soon as he left she went over to Emily to comfort her. Emily was giving birth to her seventh son on Madam's birthday, which made her very happy.

Master dropped the boys at Pastor Martin's quarters and went to fetch Willie and Miss Lilly again. When they arrived the baby was almost born. All Willie had to do was guide the baby out. Madam had walked her right through the birth of her seventh son.

Master started to explain to Madam as to why he was in Emily's room.

"Uh, Madam, I heard a noise earlier and it sounded like crying, so I came over to see if my help was needed," he said. When I left, you were sleeping and I didn't want to wake you."

She let him go on and on with his explaining, but she knew the truth.

I was surprised they let Madam stay in the slave quarters while Emily was having the baby. White women were not allowed in the slave quarters. That was the white man's law. Maybe Master was just too ashamed to tell her to leave. After all, it was her birthday and he didn't want to hurt her feelings. The baby was another son, and Madam was proud. This child looked so much like Joel Edward,

Madam's son. Master named him Edward Leon Hoover. This was the only child of Emily's that he gave his name, and raised in the big house as a white child.

He privately wished that he had given all of sons the name Hoover, after finding out that Madam couldn't have any more children.

"This one is mine," said Madam.

Emily looked surprised. Madam wrapped him up.

"Get Emily cleaned up and bring her and her things into the big house to the master bedroom," she said to Miss Lilly.

She took the baby with her to the big house. She went straight to the bedroom where she placed little Edward Leon in her son's bed, to sleep right next to her.

Emily was too tired to feel hurt or sad, she thought, "Little Edward Leon Hoover was going to stay in the big house."

Master told all of the slaves on the plantation that Madam Charlotte had given birth to another child to cover his next lie and that was to raise this child as his own.

When they got over to the big house with Emily, Master and Madam were both waiting with the baby. Emily had accepted the idea that they wanted to raise him as a Hoover. Emily thought that giving her son to the woman who had raised her as her own daughter was the least she could do. Madam didn't have Master's love, she couldn't have more babies, and she couldn't be with her true love, Percy Carson. Emily felt like she gave some happiness to Madam by giving her another baby to care for as her own.

Besides, Emily was deeply in love with Master. They were starting to act more like husband and wife. They lived on the ranch for many years like a married couple.

Master was delighted that Madam took Emily's child as their son. She did what he wanted to do. He couldn't because he didn't want to hurt Emily. When Emily appeared happy about Madam taking the baby, he was surprised. That made him love her even more.

He started acting like a child with a new toy. He was the happiest man on earth that day. While he was jumping around like a little kid, the boys saw him and they were happy too.

He got busy writing an article to put in his newspaper. He now had part ownership of the newspaper. He bought half the shares in the Morning Sun Newspaper to help the widow continue running it. I think he felt guilty because of what his father had done years ago. He thought of putting an announcement about his new son in the paper, saying that his wife Madam Charlotte had given birth to her second son. That was what he wanted to do, and that is just what he did, announcing that they had named him Edward Leon.

"And the deceit goes on," he thought.

He knew that in a few decades no one could possibly sort it out.

Emily went every day to breast feed little Edward Leon. One day when she finished, she got up to leave.

"Sit down, we need to talk," said Madam.

"Yes Madam." Emily replied.

She sat down next to Madam.

"I hear that slavery is going to end soon, and I am happy about that. I will miss you and the boys if you ever left this place."

Emily looked surprised.

"Oh, Madam you have no idea how much I would miss you if I ever had to leave this place. I love you so much," she said.

She got ready to leave and return to her quarters.

Abruptly, Madam Charlotte said,

"Wait a minute Emily, I haven't finished yet. I want you to know something that I've known for quite some time about you and Master. I know that you are lovers and that all of the boys were fathered by him."

Emily was totally surprised; she felt ashamed and speechless.

Madam continued,

"I love you. I raised you like a daughter. You have been so good and attentive to my needs, and I know you love me too. For that I am thankful. Don't get me wrong, at first I was so angry with both of you, but as time passed I understood. I knew that Master didn't love me. We were best friends when we were school age. He told me everything about the girl from Chicago back then. He came home from college and told me about a girl that he was so much in love with. A girl that he described to me as a light skinned colored girl. That girl could have been you Emily. I think I knew it when he first brought you here, but I loved you too. You were so cute and innocent. I knew in my heart keeping you and taking good care of you was the best way of keeping both of you forever."

Madam continued, "Master never really made love to me before that night, when he thought he was making love to you. He doesn't know that I know that, because I never told him. He was calling out your name. So you see, your coming into our lives helped us both have a life, without hurting each other. You know, I feel like your sons are a part of me. They are like my grandchildren."

Emily was so surprised that she began to cry.

"Don't cry. You sit here and listen to the whole story about Master and me; how my marriage was arranged. After this you can go on and feel free to love him," Madam said.

Then she told her that Master had really never loved her. She told her about the $10,000 payment her father made to arrange the marriage.

"I was hoping he would fall in love with me, but he never did." She went on to say, "Master Hoover really loves you, I could tell by the way he looks at you," she said.

Neither Madam Charlotte nor Emily knew that he was listening to their private conversation outside the door.

Emily was speechless. In her mind she was thinking, "All

those years she knew and never said anything. She must love me as much as I love her."

"Madam, I am so sorry," she said. "In the beginning I was told that I was helping you by doing whatever Master told me to do."

"Emily, you were helping me, and because of that we have eight wonderful sons together."

"Please, Madam let me finish. After a few years I knew better. I had fallen in love with him and couldn't stop myself. I still love him, today more than ever. Master is the only man that treated me like a person. I felt bad about not being able to tell you the truth. You were like a mother to me and the one person that I would never want to hurt."

Madam knew she didn't need to ask her for the baby then. She wanted to anyway, before she had already taken the baby without asking.

"I want to raise Edward Leon as my son. I want to raise him as a white child," she said. "But if you ever leave this place, I want you to know that he will not be leaving with you."

"I would be pleased and honored to have you raise little Edward Leon as your son. Mama you raised me and I am happy. I hope that he makes you proud of him someday. I feel that's the least that I could do for you." Emily had no intention of ever leaving the ranch, but she didn't say that to Madam.

Just as she was ready to give Madam a kiss and leave, Master walked in the door. He pretended not to have heard their conversation.

"Emily has given her son to us, to be raised as a white child," Madam told Master. She didn't want him to continue thinking that she had taken the baby.

"What do you think about raising Edward Leon as a white child?" she asked.

"I think it's a great idea, especially since we gave him my name." Master replied.

Then Master Hoover said to Emily, "If you decide to do this, you can never speak of it to anyone. The secret must never come out."

"It would make me proud to know my son is being raised by both of you, but what will I tell his brothers?" She asked.

"The boys are so young now. The only one that might want to know more would be Clarence," replied Master. Since he was only six years old then, maybe he would forget soon, just like the others. They all hoped that Emily's other sons would think Edward Leon was Joel Edward's brother, and their uncle.

"Just don't talk about it to him now and don't ever talk about it to them in the future. Then they will remember whatever we tell them," said Master.

Emily couldn't promise that she would lie to her sons. She made up her mind that all of her sons would know the truth about their family. She did promise not to tell the secrets to anyone else outside the family.

As they grew up, she told all of her sons, except Edward Leon, that Master was their father. Edward Leon was raised to believe that he was the child of Madam Charlotte and Master Hoover.

"We are all still together now and we will remain together as long as slavery is still here. If slavery is no more and you wish to stay on the ranch, this is your home forever," said Master. He also told her that through the years he fixed it so none of her sons would ever live like colored people.

"I would be very sad if you left. I always felt we would be together forever," said Madam.

I stood there speechless, watching those women. I realized they were inseparable. They played Master off pretty well. It's just too bad Master overheard their conversation.

Madam Charlotte and Emily were two very brave and wonderful women.

Emily stood up and thanked them both for all of their love and support. She then went over to her son's bed and picked him up. She held him close and kissed him. I heard her whisper to him that she would always love him and she would never leave him unless she died and went to live with God. Then she laid him back down in his little bed as Madam watched her.

After they finished talking, Emily left and Madam went over to the baby's bed. She picked up Edward Leon, held him close and kissed him, whispering to him that she was always going to protect him as long as she lived.

Master left right away because he thought Emily was upset and he followed her to her quarters. I think he wanted to know if she was going to keep Madam's secret of knowing everything about their love affair. When he got to her quarters she was crying. He walked in and put his arms around her.

"I feel so bad about what we've done for so many years. It hurt Madam. I'm afraid our sons may suffer for the mistakes we've made." she said.

"No they won't. My sons will never become slaves," he said. He promised her that he would always protect his sons, even in his grave.

"I've made plans to protect all of them forever. There's only one catch, and that is you. It's up to you to make sure their secrets are kept safe forever."

"Oh no, those secrets won't get told to anyone outside the family," she promised.

He remembered that she never told him a word of what they were saying because Madam asked her not to tell him. That's when he knew that she could be trusted with the master plan.

The deceit goes on. He never realized that trying to protect his sons would be the most disastrous plan of all.

7

I fell asleep again, but when I opened my eyes this time I saw my sister trying to talk to me. I was deep into my own thoughts. I never answered. She turned and walked out of the room. I felt bad about not answering her, but I knew that if I stopped I would lose my connection back in time.

I could hear my sister talking about me to my best friend in the other room. "Leave her alone," my friend was saying." She is really obsessed with her past." I didn't want to listen to them. Soon I couldn't hear their voices anymore.

I opened my eyes and saw that the Civil War had come. Master Hoover had done a good job of keeping his sons a secret from the world, and protecting them, or so he thought. He made sure that all of Emily's boys could pass for white if they wanted to. Not just the child he'd given his name to, but all of them. His deceit was done well. Everyone in town thought his boys were white; none knew a Mulatto slave was their mother.

He had no choice but to continue the deceit when all the young men were enrolled in the Army.

"They are my sister's sons from Chattanooga, Tennessee. She passed away. Her husband was killed in a fight by outlaws. The boys had no one left but me. I raised them along with my own two sons," he explained.

Before going off to war, Joel Edward, Madam's son, got married. His wife became pregnant. Emily's son, Evan Lee, became a father also, naming his son Peter Joe, after his favorite brother.

The boys were sent to war. The Hoover boys were in the First Battle of Bull Run. The Confederate troops, reinforced in time, won a resounding victory.

General Irvin McDowell prepared 130,000 men to challenge Lee, whose army of 60,000 was massed in Virginia near Fredericksburg.

The letter arrived shortly after the battle in Virginia.

Dear Mr. Hoover,

We regret being the bearer of this news about your sister's sons. They were killed in Battle in Virginia.

Peter Joe Allen, Willie Leroy Allen, and David Roy Allen have died bravely; we pray they rest in peace.

There is some good news. We are happy to inform you that your sister's son Joel Jon Allen, who was found wounded, is alive, and will be home soon.

Regretfully,

Confederate Army

Below the signature a note was added that said:

JUST IN TODAY —

While writing you this letter, we regret this notation regarding your firstborn son, Mr. Hoover. Your son Joel Edward was also killed in battle. It was just one day after his cousins. Just today the list of the soldiers killed in battle came across my desk, and your son's name appeared on the list of casualties.

The news was so painful; it knocked Master off his feet.

Lee lost nearly one-fifth of his men and General, Stonewall Jackson.

Master Hoover lost his only white son, and three sons by the woman he loved. He cried like a baby when he got the news.

"It was my fault," he thought. I was responsible for all four of my Allen boys being in the armed forces, with all my lies and secrets.

He'd enlisted Emily's boys, but Charlotte's son Joel Edward didn't have to go to war. It was his decision to go, to join in the fight for justice.

This news almost killed Master. He started to get weaker and weaker as the days went by. Master and Madam Charlotte were up in age by this time. They had been doing well for elderly people. Emily was almost 25 years younger. After they got the news about the boys, they all seemed to deteriorate. They were heartbroken and speechless for months.

Emily wandered around the ranch alone, looking at the horses, not wanting the others to see the pain in her face. The boys liked the horses.

Her son, Joey Jon was still in the Army. She had fears about him being killed too. The Army said in the letter that he was coming home soon. She still couldn't face the fact that three sons were dead. She was afraid to feel happy about Joey Jon because she feared it would cause him to die too.

I was surprised to see that same fear in her that was in me. I, too, was afraid of happiness. I feared that bad things would happen if I were happy. My memories were returning day-by-day.

Emily couldn't smile, until one day Joel Jon, his wife, and their new baby girl showed up at the door. She looked up at her son's beautiful face, and lit up like a Christmas tree. Through all her pain this made her happier than she had ever been.

His wife, Jacqueline, who was white, was completely aware of his ethnicity. Emily had never seen her granddaughter before, and was thrilled to find out they named the baby after her. She loved little Emily the instant she saw her.

It seemed during that time Master was very sick. He was not going out with his friends like he used to. The loss of his sons devastated him.

I remembered what Big Daddy said about him. "A man that was so strong just fell apart overnight," he said while reminiscing about family stories as I sat near him on the porch.

Master couldn't stop thinking about how he lied to get his sons into the Army. He thought about the men that he was involved with in the HMC Club. They took the lives of innocent people just because they were different. He knew the seeds that he had planted in his life were now growing back into the lives of his loved ones. He never really understood that old saying, "you reap what you sow."

"If only I'd told the truth," he kept repeating to himself. "I used my best friend to help get those boys into the United States Army by lying to them. I told them my sons were my sister's children just to get them accepted as white men."

He promised Emily that their sons would never live like slaves and he would protect them forever. He even lied to his sons and never got a chance to tell them the truth. These tragedies left Master Hoover, Madam Charlotte, and Emily heartbroken for many years. It was said that Master never really recovered from it.

I found myself sleepy again. In no time the war was over. "The war is over, we are free, we are free at last!" People were shouting... I looked around and everyone was all dressed up. They looked like they were going on a trip or moving to a new place. People were running around, crowds of people were all over the place and I wondered where they all came from. I had never seen so much excitement in the streets before. Then I thought...

These were the only sons still alive: Clarence Allen, Evan Lee Allen, Joey Jon Allen, and Edward Leon Hoover. They found a way, through the strength of Emily, to go on into the future carrying the pain of a family lost at war.

8

I walked around looking for something that showed the date. I looked on the table and I saw a newspaper.

Just as I ran over to look, I saw Emily's son, Clarence, pick it up. He began reading to Miss Lilly. The war had ended and the slaves were freed, but the pain would not end so quickly.

"Over 600,000 people have been killed," he read. Even more were wounded." A haunted look entered his eyes.

"I really miss my brothers."

Clarence finally mentioned to Rosa that it was 1865. He still felt a deep sadness. He started naming off the loved ones and friends who had been lost in the war.

"I'm glad it's over," he said finally.

After slavery, the Hoovers had given their freed slaves the homes that they were living in, in exchange for continuing to work on the plantation. Each family had separate little huts on the plantation with two rooms and a kitchen. No stove or ice box. They used buckets with blocks of ice to keep their milk and butter cool.

Miss Lilly used to cook for both the big house and the slaves. Willie would pick up the food for the slaves every day and take it to their quarters.

I drifted off again. Opening my eyes again, I started looking for Emily or anyone that I knew. When I saw the ranch I ran over to Miss Lilly's and looked in the door. She looked about 90 years old. "It must be the late 1800s," I thought.

Miss Lilly looked so lonely. I looked for her husband Willie, but he was not there. She was sitting in the big rocking chair reading the paper. Miss Lilly and Willie now had a nice two-bedroom house on the plantation, built just for them. They practically ran the plantation, and were like family to the Hoovers. They had come to trust and need Willie and Miss Lilly.

Suddenly I saw two people coming into the room from the kitchen. I realized it must be Emily's first son Clarence and his wife Rosa. Rosa was Miss Lilly's daughter. I saw a young man. I thought he was their son.

"Hello Peter Joe," Clarence and Rosa said simultaneously. I realized it was Evan Lee's son, named after his brother who died in the war.

"Peter Joe, what a nice friendly name. I wish I could get to know him." I thought.

His father, Evan Lee, was close to his brothers, but he was especially close to Peter Joe. Evan Lee had been sick a lot when they were growing up, so he couldn't always do his chores. Peter Joe would look after him and help Evan Lee finish his chores. Peter Joe even got in trouble for Evan Lee with Master Hoover one day, and took his punishment. Evan Lee never forgot that, and when his son was born, he named him after his brother. He came home on leave once before he was killed. He was so proud of his namesake, little Peter Joe. Clarence was reminiscing with his wife Rosa, even though I believe she knew about a lot of it. Although she was with him during this time, I don't think she knew the details of some family secrets. Rosa and I were already sitting there listening to him tell the story, but she didn't know that I was on the floor next to her listening too.

Clarence began:

"Mama Emily couldn't rest late one night and she went into Master's room to check on him. She found him not feeling well. She decided to give him his morning bath, hoping that it would make him feel better. She noticed that while she was bathing him, he was falling asleep right in the middle of his bath. Mama Emily knew that wasn't like him, because he still enjoyed her touch, even though he was an old man. She knew he would never go to sleep while she was touching his body. His body was very warm."

"I remembered that she called me, very concerned.

"Is something wrong?" I asked.

"Yes, I think so. Master seemed very weak while taking his bath, and he may have a fever."

I noticed that Master was weak, but thought it was because he was up in his 90s.

He hadn't been able to get out of bed on his own for two years now. I remembered it well, because Mama Emily was trying to take care of running the house and everyone else. I worried about her health. After all, she was 72.

"I was 51 myself and I wanted to help. But she still tried to do everything herself. Madam Charlotte was 88 years old. Everyone was surprised that she had lived that long because of her rare blood disease. Mama Emily was not ready to let go of either one of them. So for years she made sure that they ate well, and had their regular doctor's visit."

"I could hear Mama Emily calling one of us to come with the carriage, because it was time to get the doctor. Mama Emily always called him 'Edward' or 'Master.' We all knew the truth by now because she told us. They never told the boys that were killed in the war. All three died without knowing the truth. They also never told Edward Leon, her seventh son."

Master didn't want to tell Edward Leon the truth about his mixed blood. The boys were all told about Mama Emily being a nanny in the big house. Edward Leon was told that she was his father's bed warmer only when he was older. Even then Master Hoover didn't tell him she was his mother. When the boys were small, he told them she was his sister, and later he told them another lie. He lied so much, until his sons didn't know what to believe.

"Mama Emily told her boys the truth when the Civil War ended. Master still didn't want to tell the truth. Master said he was going to tell Edward Leon the truth after the war was over, but he never did."

He told so many other lies. We were forbidden to tell Edward Leon about the secrets. So, now that Master was on his sickbed and might die, it looked like he was going to take the secrets to his grave without telling the only son that carried the family name.

"I thought that if he kept those secrets from Edward Leon, it was going to be a curse on both the Allens and the Hoovers. That didn't matter to him. Keeping his family white was more important than worrying about a family curse. I knew why my father liked to call himself 'The Master of Deceit.' "Madam even wanted to tell Edward Leon the truth, but he forbade her to."

"While I was growing up, I watched my mother looking after Edward Leon around the clock. Mama Emily acted just like a real daughter to Madam. Just like a real wife to Master. She had been taking care of them for so many years. Nobody believed she was anything but part of the Hoovers. She looked white. So she had a good chance of living as a white lady all of her life, and she did."

He paused for a moment, then continued.

"People in the community knew she took care of Madam and the Master. Some were told that she was Master's sister, and others were told she was his daughter. No one really cared who she was, just what she was - black or white?

I watched her going in and out of his room that day after his bath."

"'Son, go into town quickly and fetch me the doctor because Master is burning up with fever and I can't get it down,' " she said.

So I ran out to the barn and got the carriage. I saw Evan Lee fixing one of the horse's shoes. Evan Lee was the caretaker for the horses, now that old Willie had gone to meet his maker. When I told him about the emergency, he jumped in the carriage and off we went.

"While we were gone Mama Emily worked to get the fever down but had no luck. When we returned she was almost in tears. She was sitting in a chair next to his bed with her head down, praying for the man she loved."

Rosa and I were really enjoying Clarence's story-telling. We just sat back and went with the flow of the story.

He went on to say, "When we arrived with the doctor and walked into the room, Mama Emily ran to Dr. Pitts to tell him that Master was very ill. Even though Dr. Pitts was quite old and retired by now, he was still the best doctor in town."

"Don't worry about Master Hoover,' Dr. Pitts said. 'This old fox is not ready to go yet."

"Dr. Pitts went to the bed to examine him. He came prepared and brought medicine for Master's high fever. After finishing his examination and giving him the medicine, he decided to sit with him and wait. He never stirred for two hours; then he awoke. His fever had gone down. Dr. Pitts waited another hour, sitting with family at his bedside. Emily was in the room the whole time."

Clarence explained something to Rosa and me, even though he didn't know I was listening.

"I wondered what Madam thought about being left out of the room from her husband. I found out from her myself. I asked her if she wanted me to help her into his room. I only did that because I thought she felt bad."

"Madam answered, 'I'm doing alright son. Emily is the one who should be in the room with him now anyway." Then she told me she couldn't help him now because she was too old. Their daughter Emily was doing a good job taking care of them both.

"After waiting another hour, Dr. Pitts fell asleep and Emily prayed."

"'Hello there beautiful.' Hearing the voice, she looked up, and it was Master trying to sit up in bed.

"'Hello there you old fox,'" said Dr. Pitts.

"'I wasn't talking to you! You old goat.'" he said. They all laughed. He felt pain in his chest and had to lie back in bed.

"Dr. Pitts was examining him again, when suddenly he really started to have trouble breathing. Emily was afraid and began to cry.

"'Get your sons right away Emily,'" said Dr. Pitts.

"Emily ran out to fetch her sons, and in moments we were all in the room together."

"'Take your mother out and keep her there until I come see you,'" said Dr. Pitts to Evan Lee. The doctor knew Master was having a heart attack and he was trying to keep Emily from getting too upset. He was hoping he could get it under some kind of control."

"'Clarence, help me lift him,'" Dr. Pitts said. 'We need to get him into a sitting position so he can get some air.'"

"He gave him an injection to make him relax. After the doctor got control of the situation, he waited with me for half an hour. Master was resting comfortably. He went back to sleep.

"When Dr. Pitts came out of the room he could tell that Emily was frightened. He knew that he had to tell her the truth.

"Master Hoover had a heart attack and he is resting," he said. 'You need to start calling all of the family members who are away because he may only be with us another two weeks, and that's putting it generously because he is very weak now.' Emily stood, dazed. Madam and the others were terribly sad."

"I'll get in touch with the others for you Mama Emily," I told her."

"At that time Rosa and I, Miss Lilly, Evan Lee, his wife Elaine, their son Peter Joe, Pastor Martin, his wife Sister Harriet, and their two sons John and David Martin all lived in the home together.

"Anyone from other plantations who wanted to share was welcome to come on Sundays to the large church they'd built to praise the Lord. The pastor was well known in the community as a great speaker, and his wife Harriet could sing the gospel like nobody else. If times were different, she would have traveled the world singing gospel songs.

"Pastor and Harriet Martin could have left Hoover Ranch any time they wanted with the end of slavery. Since Sister Harriet started the children's choir, which they called 'The Divine Healing Ministry.' She didn't want to leave them. She traveled with the children's choir all around the area visiting with other community youth groups."

I was really enjoying this family history, and was so glad

that Clarence wasn't tired. He continued with the story:

"Emily went over to Madam and put her arms around her.

"'Now sweetheart you knew this was coming. You need to be strong for me because my time is coming soon also,'" said Madam.

"'Mother what's wrong? Are you all right?'" She asked.

"'I'm fine, but I'm an old woman now,' she replied. 'Now, you must listen to me. Master and I have loved you since the day we met. Now I need your help.' She paused. 'There is something very important that I must tell Master Hoover before he dies, and you must be strong for the rest of us.'"

"'I'll be strong for you, Madam,' she said. 'I'll always love the both of you.'"

"'Okay sweetheart! Now, Emily this is what we are going to do. Whenever he wakes up I want you to go in with him and tell him your good-byes. Then I want you to tell him that I want to see him alone, to say my own good-bye to him.' She wondered what Madam had on her mind because she was acting so secretive.

"Dr. Pitts didn't leave. He just went over to the corner where Master Hoover kept his big rocking chair, and went to sleep. Emily went to sit with Master until he awakened. She did exactly what Madam told her. Madam wanted to make sure he didn't die before she had her say.

"When I came back into the room, I told my grandmother that I sent messages to everyone who lived in the states. I sent messages to all the family in California, Washington, D.C., and Chicago. Edward Leon, who lived in Washington D.C., told me he would send telegrams to the others who were out of the country." Madam was pleased with what I had done.

"'Master is awake. He's asking to see the doctor alone,'" Emily said. Evan Lee went over to the big chair and awakened the doctor.

"The doctor went into the room and closed the door behind him. Master wanted to know from the doctor if he was dying.

"'Why is my chest in so much pain?' He asked. 'It's hurting so much I can hardly breathe.'"

"'You've had a heart attack,' Dr. Pitts told him."

"'Am I getting ready to die? How long do I have?'"

"'My old friend, you're not doing so well,' said Dr. Pitts gently. 'I must tell you that another heart attack could come at any time.'"

"'You old goat, you better keep your hands off Emily when I'm gone. I know you've been wanting her for a long time.' Dr. Pitts laughed."

"'Edward you've been a lucky man, you old fox. Having two such beautiful and wonderful women in your life.' He shook his head. 'You listen here, don't you worry about Emily. She don't love or want any man but you, you lucky dog.'"

"'Alright now, that's enough. How long do I have?'"

"'Well Ed, maybe two weeks, and maybe more, but that's putting it out there.'"

"'Listen you old goat, don't you leave this house until I check out, you hear?'"

"'I'm not going anywhere,' said Dr. Pitts. 'Look here, I plan to stay awhile.'"

"'On your way out, tell Emily to come in. I'll see you in the morning,' said Master."

Clarence had a way of story-telling like my Big Daddy, and my spirit loved listening to him.

"Dr. Pitts walked into the other room and found Madam Charlotte talking to Emily."

"'Edward wants you, Emily,' said Dr. Pitts."

"She looked into the old doctor's eyes, hoping to find some kind of hope for her lover, but all she saw was death. She got up slowly and sadly. As she walked toward his door she looked back at Madam."

"'Be strong, Emily,' said Madam. She waved her on into the room. Madam knew the pain that Emily would face soon enough. Percy Carson had passed away two years earlier.

As Emily entered the room, Master was sitting up in bed with two pillows behind his back. He looked toward the door, and saw her standing there."

"'Hello! Sweetheart! Come on over here closer to me and don't be afraid.'

She looked at him for a moment, thinking how wonderful he looked. He didn't seem to be sick or dying. She walked over to him and laid her head on his chest. He hugged her very tightly in his arms."

"'How about giving this old man a bath?' He asked. He always liked feeling her hands touching his body all over, even at 98 years old."

"'Edward I would like to give you a bath, but only if you promise to behave,' she said."

"'How would an old goat like me misbehave?' He smiled at her, and she smiled back."

"'Try not to get too excited. Remember your heart - I don't want to lose you yet.'"

"'Oh, sweetheart, I don't want to ever leave you, but I know I must. I am taking you with me in my heart and I will be waiting for you for all eternity.'"

"'Master, you know I don't like that kind of talk. She leaned closer to him, fighting tears. 'I will come to you one day, my love.'"

"They held each other for a moment and then, with tears in her eyes, went into the bathroom to get his bath ready. As she settled her emotions, she filled the wash pan with warm water. He had tears in his eyes also. She began to bathe him. She washed him all over with very warm water, and a soft cloth."

"'I still enjoy the touch of your soft hands,' he said. 'I wish old bud down there would do what it used to do when you touch it. I wish I could have you just one more time.'"

"'I love you too, but I don't want you getting one bit excited, so calm down or I will let Dr. Pitts come in here and bathe you.'"

"Master Hoover laughed at that. 'I would surely die if that old codger tried to bathe me. If I died right at this moment with your hands touching me, I would say what a way to go.'"

"She finished his bath. 'Now, Emily, would you tell Madam to come talk to me, because I have some things I need to talk over with her,' he said."

"She agreed. 'She asked if you would see her because she also has things to talk over with you.'"

"She hugged and kissed him and turned to walk out of the room. When she got to the door, she looked back at him just lying in bed. He looked good to her; not like a sick man at all. He can't be dying, she told herself."

I thought my Big Daddy could tell stories well, but Clarence Sr. had him beat. After all, he probably taught my Big Daddy. Clarence told the story so well that soon we didn't even notice him talking. It seemed like we were there, inside his story.

9

Clarence continued the story:

"Emily came to Madam. 'Master is asking for you,' she said."

"When she entered his room he was sitting up and looking like the picture of health. Madam put her arms around him."

"'You're looking much better,' she said."

"'Thank you Madam. I asked to see you because I have something to say to you before I check out of here,' he said quietly."

"'That's good,' she said. I'm hear to listen. I also have something that I need to tell you.'"

"'My dear Charlotte, I'm so sorry that I was not able to be the husband you deserved. His eyes were moist. 'I'm asking your forgiveness for hurting you all these years.' When he finished she had tears in her eyes."

"'Edward, at least your dream came true. She looked into his eyes. 'I didn't want you to get away from me either, before asking you to forgive me too. I have also hurt you for many years.'"

"He may have been sick but he still had a good memory."

"'Charlotte what in the devil are you talking about? Are you talking about Emily?'"

"'No, Edward, I am not talking about Emily. Remember when we were kids, and we were best friends? You told me about the half-white colored girl in Chicago? You were away in college.'"

"'Yes I remember.'"

"'Well, when you told me about her it was the same day that our fathers arranged our marriage.'"

"'Yes, go on. So what?' He sounded a little impatient."

"'Okay! Stop interrupting me and please just listen. Madam went on to say, 'I was in love with you for the longest time, but I was afraid to tell you for fear of losing my best friend forever.'"

"'That's when I knew I could never tell you my feelings. After you told me about the girl that you loved - I will never forget your words, 'I will never love any girl, but her.' I knew then I had lost you forever as a lover. We were still best friends, so I settled for that. I decided we would be best friends forever.'"

"'You said, 'I don't want to marry you, Charlotte, because you are my best friend. Friends don't marry best friends, unless they are in love, and we are not in love.' Remember, I asked you why not? And you answered, 'Because I want to have a best friend forever.' And that's when I told you that I had an idea.'"

He smiled. Charlotte had always been a dear friend to him.

"'This idea would help you have the girl of your dreams and keep your best friend at the same time. I felt that I had lost Percy Carson, forever, so I was going to settle for a life with my best friend with no romance. Maybe in my head I was hoping you'd fall in love with me, but either way, I wanted to marry you.'"

"'Let's play a game with our parents and trick them,' I said. Do you remember that?'"

"'I remember that day very well,' he said."

"'Well, I told you we could pretend to be married just to keep your father from taking away your inheritance, and then you could go and get your girl from Chicago.'"

"'I remember you telling me about an idea you had, but I'm not clear anymore about the rest of the conversation.' He wanted her to get to the point. 'Madam, what are you trying to tell me?'"

"'Emily has been your dream for years. I've known about you two almost from the beginning.' He wasn't surprised. He was too tired to act like he was. He'd overheard her telling Emily many years ago that she knew. She still had to tell him the most important part, so she spoke a little faster. 'All I'm asking, as your best friend, is that you listen to everything I'm trying to tell you. After our marriage we all signed a marriage certificate at father's house. I was supposed to take it to the Marshall's office the next day for filing?'"

"She pulled their marriage certificate out of her pocket. She handed it to him. It should have had a stamp confirming the marriage, but he noticed that it had not been registered.

His arranged marriage to her had been a pretend marriage all those years! He really was shocked now. He had been single all his life, and never knew it. The only woman he'd ever really wanted to marry was Emily. And he could have! He felt sad, and wondered if this was her way of hurting him for all the lies and deceit he subjected her to during their long marriage."

"Does she want to get her revenge, now that I'm on my deathbed? He wondered. If so, it's working. Knowing that he could have married Emily hurt him badly."

"All my sons could have been given my name," he thought. Of course, I deserved what she did to me for all the bad things I did to her. He was determined not to be angry with her. Besides, he wanted her to forgive him."

"'When you brought Emily to the ranch, I decided not to file that certificate,' she said. He was overwhelmed by what she had just told him."

"'Edward, you should marry Emily before you die, and make everything right with God.'"

"My soul could be saved after all, he told himself when he heard Madam Charlotte's plan."

"'You know, I would love to marry Emily, but if it will hurt you in any way I will not,' he said."

"'I wouldn't be alive if it wasn't for her,' she said. 'For years, it seems like you and Emily were married anyway. I'm sorry I didn't forgive you sooner.'"

"'I could only dream about this, and before I die it will actually happen,' he said."

"Lord knows Emily deserves happiness,' she said."

"They decided to surprise Emily by holding a secret, private marriage ceremony. They only wanted family there, but Dr. Pitts was considered family so he was invited.

Madam had to let Rosa and Miss Lilly in on the secret because she needed their help planning the wedding. There wasn't much time. They just had a few days.

Master began to feel better. Happiness motivated him to fight for his life, but he was still in trouble and his heart remained weak.

The next day Emily came to give him his morning bath. He was smiling, and sitting up in bed reading a romantic novel called "How to Love Forever."

"She saw Madam Charlotte emerge from her talk with Master the day before, in a cheerful mood."

"It must be because they confessed everything and forgave each other. There are no more secrets between them,' she thought."

"She prayed to God for years, asking his forgiveness for having children with another woman's husband."

"Come Emily, give me a kiss,' he beckoned."

"'Master what's going on? What happened between you and Madam?'"

"'Stop calling me Master.'" He took her hand. 'Emily, please forgive me for not telling you to stop calling me that a long time ago.' She looked uncertain, wondering what had happened between him and Madam.'"

"'Nothing happened. We just forgave each other for the wrong doing we did, and the pain we caused each other. I must say, that made me feel free and wonderful.'"

"'Master - I mean Edward - I want to be forgiven too, for all the things that I did to cause this to happen between us. I loved you from the beginning.' She wanted to confess her sins to God, so she asked, 'I wonder, would you be with me when I confess to Pastor Martin?'"

"'I'd love to, if I can get out of bed,' he said."

"'If it's alright with you, Pastor Martin will come to the house to see us,' she said."

"'Fine! Fine! I have some questions to ask Pastor Martin myself.'"

"Nothing could have worked out better. Miss Lilly and Rosa were wondering how they could get Pastor Martin into Master's room with Emily, without her figuring out they were up to something.

Two days later everything was in place. The pastor and his wife knew it was a surprise wedding. They already had the marriage certificate.

Emily Allen and Master Hoover would finally join as husband and wife after 58 years of love and having seven sons together. Madam was glad she was still there to see it. All the family members arrived from different cities, thinking they were coming for a funeral."

I was truly enjoying this day.

Clarence continued the story:

"They were all caught up in the wedding, and had forgotten about Master dying. They even forgot that the family members coming from out of town thought it was to see him before he died.

"We saw the carriage coming toward the house from town," said Clarence . "It was Madam's daughter-in-law Eva, and her daughter Charlotte, from California, Joel Edward's only child. He died before seeing his daughter.

Mama Emily sent me and Evan Lee back and forth to the train station to pick up family members.

The Hoovers from Washington, D.C. came, Edward Leon, his wife Sheila Mae, and son Edward Earl. The only family that still lived on Hoover Ranch were Clarence, his wife Rosa, her 85-year-old mother, Miss Lilly, Evan Lee and his wife, Elaine. Out back in the slave quarters were Pastor John Martin, his wife Sister Harriet, and their sons John Junior and David."

"They were all there just in time for a wedding that they didn't know was scheduled. Rosa was trying to keep the wedding a secret. Miss Lilly tried to tell each couple as they walked through the door. It seemed to be great news to everyone except Edward Leon, who still didn't know the truth about Emily.

Edward Leon thought Emily was his nanny, and there were other lies that his father told him. He didn't know what to believe. Even though he loved her, he didn't want to be colored.

Edward Leon lived his entire life as a white man. He was not happy with his father for doing what he thought was shameful for a white man to do. He chose to marry a slave woman."

"'I came only out of respect for my mother. She is losing Master,' he said. 'I knew they didn't live their lives as a married couple because of my father's love affair with Mama Emily.'" He was teaching his son, Edward Earl, not to associate himself with colored people. He didn't know he was a colored man himself."

"'Emily, please wear my wedding dress to Master's confession party,' said Madam. That was what Emily was told."

"Madam didn't want Master Hoover to see her on her wedding day, or before the wedding. She contrived a reason for her to give him his bath the night before.

Edward Leon went to see Madam on the morning of the wedding."

"'Can't you stop this? It's indecent,' he said. It didn't help him."

"'No one is going to interfere with this marriage while I'm in this house,' she said. 'One day you might understand. Or, you might not. That's up to you.'"

"Miss Lilly, Rosa and Madam Charlotte all helped to dress Emily for the surprise of her life. Clarence and his other brothers, except Edward Leon, made a big to-do over Master Hoover. They dressed him in his best suit and put him in his rolling chair. They pushed him into the big party room of the church. Everyone came all dressed in their Sunday best for a big family celebration."

"Emily was proud that he was ready to ask God for forgiveness. She felt like God answered her prayers. For many years, she prayed for him to ask God's forgiveness before he died. At last, he was coming to Christ, and his whole family was attending the church service to welcome him. Or so she thought.

As the ceremony began, the guests were seated in the pews, with light shining in from the windows. The pastor and his family were waiting.

It was 11:00 a.m., and they had chairs on both sides of Master's chair, waiting for his ladies. The crowd hushed as Madam and Emily came into the room. They walked in together, holding each other's arms, as mother and daughter.

Emily wore Madam's wedding dress, with lovely white flowers in her beautiful hair. Madam wore a pretty beige satin dress trimmed in lace with attractive white flowers in her hair too. The pastor stood up."

"'Let us all prepare for prayer to bless this fellowship,'" he said."

"After the prayer he turned the meeting over to Master. His sons all stood with him. The boys pushed him up to the front of the room to speak to his family."

"'To my family members and friends: I am weak and not in the best of health, but I am the happiest man on earth today.'" He coughed slightly. 'I am leaving you all sooner than you think, and I hope you can forgive me if I have hurt any of you in the past. It is a wonderful day to be with all of you. I want you to know that what I did during my lifetime was out of love for my family. My wish is that you will all continue to protect this family, as I have tried to do.' He then said, 'What you are about to witness here today is a private family affair, not to be repeated to anyone outside this family.' He was getting weak, but he wanted to finish what he was saying. 'When I am gone I am asking you not to be sad for me. Celebrate instead.' He looked at the pastor."

"'I am ready to start,' he said."

"Everybody turned and looked at Emily. She looked behind her to see why everybody was staring. The pastor prepared to make the wedding announcement to her, since everyone else knew."

"'Dearly beloved, we are gathered here to witness the marriage of two great people, Master Edward D. Hoover to the love of his life.'"

"Emily looked at Madam, thinking they were renewing their marriage vows. 'They must have kept this a secret,' she thought. Master Hoover looked at Emily's face. His heart nearly stopped because he was excited. The moment had come to ask for God's blessing upon their union."

"The pastor began. 'Emily, would you stand and come forward with your mother?'

Emily thought she was escorting Madam to be remarried. When she got to the altar, they planned to bring Emily and Master together for their vows."

"'Step up here,' the pastor motioned to Emily.

Master passed out.

Shock overtook the church. Everybody stood up at once. Master's sons, the Pastor, and Dr. Pitts rushed to his side, but they could not arouse him. The doctor checked him."

"'Carry your father back to bed right away,' he said to his sons. Madam was devastated.

Stunned with disbelief, Emily looked at her, tears streaming from her eyes".

"'He wanted to ask God's forgiveness,' she said. 'Why now?'

Tears rolled down their faces, as they held each other. They were crying, but not for the same reasons."

"Master's last words were for us to celebrate his going, and not to be sad, so you may start to celebrate now. Then the pastor and his wife left to join the doctor."

"'Is he dead?' Everyone was whispering by now.

Emily and Madam did not move, holding each others

hand.

Edward Leon and his family didn't want to admit they were happy that the marriage didn't happen. They hoped this event would never be talked about again. They were angry at Edward Leon's father for even thinking about marrying a nigger. Half white or not, she was still a nigger to them.

Emily and Madam struggled to their feet, barely able to see as they walked together to be with Master. They both had eyes filled with tears.

"He is at peace now. He asked for forgiveness and that saved him," said Madam. Emily knew he'd asked her not to be sad, so she tried, but she felt such a sense of loss, it took her breath away.

The door to Master's room opened, and his sons came out. With the exception of Edward Leon, they all went directly to Emily to comfort her.

"It was another heart attack," her son Evan Lee told her, holding her small hand in his big strong one.

The Pastor and Dr. Pitts stood by Master's bed.

"Do you think he's going to make it," the pastor said under his breath to Dr. Pitts.

Just as Dr. Pitts prepared to answer, Master opened his eyes. Remembering that it was his wedding day, he tried to get up.

"Lay still. Don't you move," the doctor ordered. "You had another heart attack. Any more excitement will kill you."

The doctor knew that surviving even one more day was unlikely, even with rest. To keep him sedated, he prepared a shot of whiskey.

Master moved his lips. They leaned toward him to hear what he was trying to say.

"I want to talk to Pastor first," he said very softly.

Pastor Martin pulled a chair close to the bed, sitting very near so he wouldn't need to talk very loud.

"Pastor do you think your God would listen to me now?"

"God is not just my God, he is everyone's God, and if you want him in your heart, all you have to do is invite him in. 'He is always listening.' Pastor replied."

"'What should I say?' Asked Master."

"'Just open your heart and let him in.'

To everyone's astonishment, Master began to take his shirt off to show his chest. The Pastor's wife turned away quickly to avoid seeing him exposed.

Master noticed her turning away."

"'Well now Sister Harriet, I have lots of respect for God's leaders, and I ain't never tried to do nothing with you, nor would I ever do something improper in front of you.'

After taking off his shirt, he was ready to talk to God."

"'God, Pastor told me to open up my heart to you now. I want you to see my chest to prove that my heart is opened.'

Sister Harriet started to smile at him, so he stopped speaking to God for a moment to say a few words to her."

"'That's better Sister Harriet, because the only woman I ever exposed myself to was Emily, and now she is my wife. I know I didn't get a chance to marry her in the eyes of all of my children yet.' He pointed to the pastor."

"'Pastor, get me those papers. I want to sign them right now before I go.' As the pastor handed Master the papers to sign, he went right on talking."

"'Sister Harriet, come on over closer to me now. I want you to give this certificate of marriage to my best friend Madam, she will know what to do.'"

"'I'd be happy to do that for you, Master,' Sister Harriet said, and she did.

He then looked at the pastor and continued his talk with God."

"'Well, God here is my heart,' he said, patting his chest. "'Come on in now and save my old soul, but first I want to tell you something. I did do one or two good things in my life.'"

"He went on to say, 'I always took good care of Madam, even though she tells me now that we weren't married, and I never tried to have sex with her because I loved Emily. The only sex we had was her doing, and not mine.'"

"He stopped and thought for a moment. Then continued,

"'The only woman I ever really wanted was Emily, and I wished I had married her, but you know, I married her in my heart, God.'"

"He thought for a moment and concluded. 'The last thing I want to say is, you know I didn't think of them as slaves. I loved my slaves, and I was good to them.'

When he finished opening his heart to God, he looked at the pastor and asked,"

"'Do you think He heard me?'

"'God would have heard you if you just thought the words in your mind,' said the pastor.

That was surprising to the Master."

"'Well then, he knows more about my heart than I thought,' he said finally. Dr. Pitts was listening, and he wondered what Master meant when he said that."

"Then he said, 'That must account for my longevity. God must have given it to me.' The pastor nodded his head."

"'How are you feeling after your confession,' the pastor asked."

"'My soul is happy, but my chest feels like a ton of bricks is sitting on top of it. I just want some peace from this pain now.'

Sister Harriet walked over to comfort him."

"'Master Hoover I would like to sing a song for you, if that would make you feel better.'

He smiled.

She chose the perfect song for him.

She sang 'Peace in the Valley,' in a voice so rich it could have been a full choir. Everyone in the house was spellbound.

The pastor prayed for the soul of Master. Silently, gently, he reached over with his finger and closed Master's eyes. Master had gone to the other side."

"'I'm going out to tell the family that the old fox, and my dear friend, is gone,' said Dr. Pitts. They already knew. They heard his soul depart in Sister Harriet's song. As her voice filled the air, they had stood spellbound. It was as if his spirit came to each of them to say good-bye."

"When the doctor came out of the Master's room, everyone was standing near the door as quiet as a mouse."

"'He's gone home,' he said.

Emily and Madam Charlotte clung to each other in their pain, remembering his request."

"Don't be sad for me,' he said," they all tried.

They had a celebration when they laid him to rest. It was one of the biggest celebrations ever done on Hoover's Ranch. They held it in the church that Master Hoover built. Sister Harriet sang to uplift everyone with her lovely voice. They could feel Master's acceptance of this celebration in spirit. He had to be smiling. Emily and Madam were dancing with him in spirit. "It was a glorious way for him to go home."

And with that, Clarence ended his story.

I cried, listening to the story, hearing Sister Harriet's song in my mind. I sensed that Master Hoover was at peace.

I needed to go back to the future, but this was so interesting. When Clarence finished telling us the story, not one person's eyes were dry. Rosa reached out and hugged him, and so did I. Only he didn't know it. At least, I thought he didn't. He said something strange.

"Thank you, Rosa." He paused. "Rosa, I felt my father hugging me too."

"I felt something touching my hands when I was hugging you."

Then I knew it was time to get home to the future.

But before I went, I saw him put his arms around Rosa.

"Look how many family members are gone," he said. "My dad, good old Willie, Old Harry, Sweet Anna. Then the Civil War took Peter Joe, Willie Leroy, David Roy, and Joel Edward."

I found myself missing Mama Emily and Madam Charlotte, and I knew I couldn't go back yet. I wanted to see if they were lonely, because they had lost so many loved ones. The older they got, the more they missed the people they lost.

The oldest still living was Miss Lilly. She still had her good memory and still guided the younger folks. The young people always looked up to the eldest, and everyone looked up to Miss Lilly and took good care of her.

I decided to run over to the big house, where I found Emily and Madam. There they were, sitting in that beautiful front room of the house they liked to call, "the sitting room." It's was hard to look at those two ladies growing old together. They were still very attractive women, despite their advanced years. They no longer had the spark they once had. Losing Master and their sons had taken its toll.

They sat and reminisced, as old people like to do. They talked especially about how they missed and loved the same man for so many years.

Madam died on Master's birthday. The day that she died, Emily took food into her room to feed her, but she was so weak that she couldn't eat. She never really got over losing Joel Edward. Percy was gone, and her best friend, Master Hoover was no longer there for her.

"Mother is tired, and I must ask you to please let me go sweetheart," she had said to Emily in a soft voice. "You have been a perfect daughter."

It seemed so difficult for her to talk. Emily could barely hear her voice.

"Mother is weary now. Please be happy for me, and let me go now." She put her arms around her.

"Emily, I want to be at peace with my best friend. He is waiting for me now. We will be waiting for you too, dear."

Emily held her like a baby. Madam said, "I have always loved you Emily. You took good care of our boys."

She reached for a large white envelope on the table. Her old fingers couldn't quite grasp it, so Emily helped her.

"Keep it," she said. "It's from both of us."

The envelope was signed by Master Hoover and Mother Charlotte. When she opened the envelope, she saw papers.

"What are these?" She asked.

"Just look and you will see."

"But..." Her mouth dropped. The papers showed that she was married to Master Hoover.

"When I was wearing your wedding dress..." She stopped. The day Master died was meant to be her wedding day. Her eyes misted, remembering their honeymoon night by the river. Then she saw another document in the envelope. A will with the papers to the ranch. They had given the ranch to her and the children.

"Oh, Madam, he kept his promise to me," she said. A smile came over her face.

Madam was thrilled that she had lived to see that look on her daughter's face.

Emily looked into her mother's eyes and saw love. The very last expression they would share. She died with her eyes open, just like Master. Gently, Emily closed her eyes. As she held her in her arms, Madam's heart just stopped.

When Clarence found them, she was still holding her, rocking her in her arms and reminiscing about the first time she saw Madam at the front door of the plantation. She seemed oblivious to her death, and kept speaking to her.

"I remember how you stood with Master the day he bought me from the slave auction," she was saying. "My mother, it seems like yesterday you was so young. Your beauty took my breath away."

Clarence gently took her hand. She looked at him so grief-stricken.

"And now my mother is gone," she said, the finality of Madam's death overcoming her. She cried as Clarence quietly took Madam out of her arms.

I had tears in my eyes too. I couldn't picture Emily without Master Hoover, and especially without Madam Charlotte.

The Hoovers' lives still moved ahead towards the future, bringing with them their memories of Master Hoover and Madam Charlotte. At family gatherings each year, they would tell the story of their family's struggle to survive. Emily told them about her own family before she got to Hoover's Ranch. Though she had been taken from her mother, she remembered and passed that knowledge on to her children.

Evan Lee, her fifth son, married a slave girl from

Montgomery's place, named Elaine. A union which was arranged by Master Hoover before he died.

He set it up in such a way that they could pass for white, and many of them did for a time.

When people thought they were white, they didn't tell them any different. Especially while Emily was alive. That was a way of protecting her.

10

I was experimenting with closing my eyes to move ahead in time a little. I was trying to speed up time to the birth of my Big Daddy, but I wasn't having much luck.

When I opened my eyes I didn't miss very much. It was just 1888. Clarence Junior, my Big Daddy's father, had been born in 1866. He was, already 22 years old, and handsome.

Wait! Oh my goodness! He is arguing with his father about something. I sat on the porch watching them walk in the yard near the horses. I couldn't hear their words. Their body language told me they were arguing. I wanted to be able to hear them.

I ran out into the yard to get closer.

"You don't need to go gambling in town tonight," Clarence Sr. was telling his son. "Junior, you are throwing away money."

"Dad I am 22 years old and you still treat me like I am 12. I'll be back early. I am going to see my girl tonight. Not to gamble."

His father was glad to hear him say that he was not going gambling; his son had been doing too much of that. So me, with my nosy self, I decided to follow Clarence Jr.

I ran and got in the carriage. All dressed up, he looked like Clark Gable, who my spirit remembered from the future. That was my compliment to him, since he hadn't seen the future. He looked so good I wished he was my date.

When he got into town there were beautiful people every-where, all dressed up in style. It was a big to-do. Some huge party, I'll say! But when I looked through the door where Clarence Jr. was headed. It was a saloon.

"Oh my goodness, he lied to his father," I thought.

That Hoover lying was in his blood. Here comes the deceit into another generation!

This was not just any old party. It was a high rollers gambling party. Wow! I don't remember Big Daddy telling me about this!

I felt as though I could live in this time zone forever. I was really tempted too, but I knew better.

Clarence Jr. seemed to be the big man around town. I knew by now he was my great-grandfather. Everyone was calling him Mr. Allen, and he liked it. He was hot in the gambling business. One of the best gamblers in that part of the country. He even had his own special table. The ladies were all over him.

Those ladies had on the most elaborate dresses that I'd ever seen. I really wanted to be one of them just for a short time. So, I closed my eyes and made a wish. When I opened them, there I stood in an elegant red dress. I looked across the room. I was watching myself standing there.

"How can this be?" I wondered.

As I looked across the room my eyes stopped on Clarence Jr. He was getting ready to play another hand of cards, but when he looked up his eyes found mine. We couldn't take our eyes off each other.

He stood up at his table.

"Deal me out," he said. He walked toward me and I felt my heart pounding.

"Oh my goodness, he's good looking," I thought. Then I thought, "If I was going to be here looking for a man, why couldn't I spot someone else. "He's my great grandfather, for God's sake, and why am I lusting after him?"

When he stepped in front of me, I was speechless. So was he for a second. We both talked at the same time. Then stopped. He reached for my hand and I gave it to him. Kissing my hand he said, "You are the most beautiful creature I have ever seen."

Well, I thought this was the best looking man I'd ever seen too. But when he put his arms around me and asked me to dance, I looked around the room and noticed the other me watching.

"Where have you been all my life?" He asked.

We smiled at each other. He held me close and we danced far into the night.

Later we went outside the saloon, and walked through town. It was a beautiful night and the moon was full. I was excited when he asked me if I wanted to go for a ride in the moonlight.

"We could see the countryside together," he said.

"Yes, I would love to see the countryside with you," I answered.

We walked over to his carriage, and he lifted me inside. When I was in his arms I felt like I was going to melt. His light brown eyes were so sexy, and his lips so kissable. I wanted to hold him and kiss his beautiful lips.

The other me just stood over there in a daze. I couldn't believe what I was seeing. "They are going to leave me if I don't hurry," I thought. So I started running. I accidentally ran right through the carriage and fell on the ground.

I was still wondering why there were two of me. "Maybe it's because of my wish," I thought. The me on the ground noticed the carriage start to move with the other me sitting close to him. I ran after the carriage. When I caught up, I just jumped right into her lap. Oh my, I found myself inside of her.

"What's your name?" He finally asked.

"Millie," I said, but he didn't hear me. The other me answered instead.

"My name is Cora Smith," she said. When she said her name, I realized that the woman wanting to make out with my grandfather wasn't me at all.

I was glad it was only my imagination too, but I do look a lot like her. I hadn't realized who she was. She would one day be my great-grandmother. When she revealed her name it broke my spell. What a relief! I didn't want to think what would have happened if I had made love to my great grandfather. I found myself smiling.

They were going riding under the moonlight, but I didn't want to go with them. I didn't want to see my great-grandfather have sex with my great-grandmother, and possibly conceive my Big Daddy. So I jumped out of the carriage and walked back to the saloon. Then I thought,

"Now what was I supposed to do all alone at the saloon where there is gambling?" So, I thought I would find a place to sleep so I could speed up time. It worked, because as soon as I looked up, I noticed that they were coming back in the carriage.

I ran near them so I could hear what they were saying. Unfortunately I ran so fast that I went right through the carriage again and made it move this time. I even made the horses jump.

"The winds are really kicking up," he said. I knew they would soon forget about the horses. They did when they started kissing. I felt a strange sensation when I went through the horses. I knew I was getting ready to go back to the future. I thought to myself, "When I start feeling things like horses, it's time to go home."

I knew if I didn't pay attention to my feelings, I might remain in the past, and I would die.

They sat in the carriage looking into each other's eyes, and their minds drifted together. They were falling in love.

Cora said, "That was a nice ride under the moonlight, and by the way Clarence, are you always this romantic?"

"Are you always such a lady?" He answered. I knew why they came back so quickly. They smiled at each other.

"I was trained to be a lady, and a good one," she said.

"Well, Cora, I am impressed with you. But there is something you need to know."

"Tell me," she said.

"I really want to see you again, but I don't know if you'll want to see me when you know who I am."

"It's funny that you said that because I was just thinking

the same thing. Okay, you go first!"

"No! Ladies first," he countered.

"Alright. I live on the Carson Plantation and I am a freed slave now. I look white because of my mother, but I am a mulatto and that means I am colored in the eyes of the law. I could pass for white if I wanted too. "

She was very surprised that he didn't get angry or even disappointed because she thought he was white. If she only knew.

Now he was more infatuated with her than ever. His family secrets weren't out in the open yet, so he didn't dare tell her he wasn't white either.

"If I tell her now, and she doesn't marry me, that could cause problems for the others," he thought. He decided not to take a chance. The deceit continued.

She could tell that he had something that he was hiding, but he wasn't ready to share it. He was acting so understanding, and yet so quiet. Finally, he thought of something to say.

"I am the son of Clarence Allen. Do you know who he is?" "Yes, I do," she said. "The Allen brothers are cousins to the Hoover's son, Edward Leon. I heard they were the richest men in these parts. I heard folks at my plantation talking about old man Hoover and Mr. Clarence Allen one day. Are you Clarence Allen Jr.?"

"Yes, I am. When can I see you next?" She was surprised that a white man in those parts would take a chance on going out with a mulatto girl. He waited patiently for her answer, but it was getting late and time for her to go home.

"Mr. Allen, it's not proper for a girl like me to be discovered dating a white man, if you know what I mean, sir." He was surprised by her answer. Then he realized that Master Hoover had protected them well.

"Madam Cora, you let me worry about that, unless you don't care to go out with me," he said.

Then he took her into his arms and kissed her passionately. She didn't know what to think. Now I saw where my grandfather learned all of his romantic moves.

The Allen boys wanted to be proud of who they were. They respected their mother and that meant being proud of her heritage. For a while they passed as white, as the Master had intended, but as each grew older decisions were made. They made choices to be colored or pass for white. Edward Leon, who didn't know that he was colored, passed. Eventually the others decided to live as colored men. Several of them joined groups that helped colored people.

I was glad that I had this journey, because it helped me remember my childhood, and along with it, the wonderful stories passed down to me by my grandfather and my mother. I realized how important it is to pass family heritage information down to each new generation.

I started to miss Mama Emily. I just couldn't get my mind off her. I felt like something bad was going to happen to her. I had to find her. I knew I should be going back to my future, but instead I closed my eyes and made a wish to go back to the Hoover Ranch Plantation.

When I opened my eyes I was in the big house with her. It was 1889, and she looked terribly sad. I was so used to seeing her with Madam Charlotte, but here she was resting all alone, in her big chair in the sitting room. I walked over and sat in the chair where Madam used to sit. She looked at me as though she could see me.

"Oh! Hello Madam," she said. "Oh my, how I've missed you." She seemed to see me, and thought I was Madam. "My goodness dear mother, you look young again. I know you are waiting for me. Don't worry I'm almost ready to come to you." I didn't know what to say. I decided not to speak. What I did not want to do was disappoint her. It felt like old times to her, being with her Madam.

"Madam Charlotte, is that going to happen to me when I get there?" She asked. I didn't know what Emily was talking about so I just shrugged my shoulders.

"Oh, Madam Charlotte you know what I am talking about. Will I get young again like you are now?" I thought she couldn't see me, but I wasn't sure anymore. I looked into her face. Oh my goodness, I didn't know what to do. She was really talking to me, and the surprise showed on my face.

Emily stopped smiling.

"Why are you so sad, Madam? Please don't worry about me because I am coming with you real soon." Then she closed her eyes and I thought she had died, so I ran into the other room to get Rosa's help, but she stopped me.

"Madam, don't leave me! I'm sorry. Sometimes I fall asleep in the middle of things."

I tried to comfort her by saying, "I remember Master falling asleep just like that." I forgot that I wasn't supposed to talk to her.

"That's right just before he died," she answered. She was smiling again. Just as she was getting ready to talk, Rosa walked into the room, looking puzzled and glancing around.

"Rosa did you lose something?" She asked. Rosa looked at her and smiled.

"Mama Emily to what or to whom are you talking?"

"As a matter of fact it's Madam," she said.

"Madam!" This concerned Rosa. Perhaps she was getting a bit senile in her old age. She pretended to clean up the area around the chair that I sat in. She looked around the room for some kind of sign that would give Emily the idea that she was talking to the spirit of Madam Charlotte. She looked at the chair that Madam used to sit in. I was in it, but she couldn't see me.

Emily laughed. I laughed too. I found myself staring at Rosa, realizing how much she reminded me of her mother, Miss Lilly.

Miss Lilly died about the time Dr. Pitts died. I missed them both.

Emily was still laughing at me. When I began to laugh she put up her hand to silence me.

"No, Madam, Rosa will get mad. Try not to let her see you laughing."

"Now Mama Emily, trying to tell me that you see Madam Charlotte, that's one thing, but telling me that she is laughing with you, is something else!"

I immediately became quiet.

"I won't tell you a thing about Madam, daughter," she said. With that, she crossed her arms and looked away.

"Mama Emily, is Rosa still harassing you?" Clarence Sr. had come in and was smiling at his mother.

"Yes, son! She loves to bother me. That wife of yours always gets after me!" They all laughed. So did I, but this time Emily didn't tell me to stop.

She loved Rosa a lot. Even if Rosa did pick on her. They played with each other all the time.

"Where are the children?" Emily asked. She just dozed off to sleep while she was talking.

"I'm worried about Mama Emily," said Rosa.

"Well she is nearly a hundred, honey."

"Clarence, I think she is ill. Maybe we should call a doctor. She falls off to sleep too often. Not only that, she was sitting here thinking she was talking to Madam Charlotte."

"Well, old folks will do that," said Clarence.

They put Mama Emily to bed. She was now sleeping in the same room Madam Charlotte and Master Hoover shared in the big house.

When I walked into that room, I still expected to see Emily breast feeding one of the boys, laughing and talking with Madam, just like the old days, but that wasn't the case this time. She slept so soundly when Clarence and Rosa laid her down. They thought it was time to call everyone home. Clarence sent a telegram to Edward Leon, who got in touch with the others.

Everyone headed home to see about her. I too, felt like I lived there with them about a century.

Her son, Joey Jon, had earned his degree in medicine. He was a doctor, but he had moved to California.

One week later, everyone arrived from all over the country. Washington, D.C., New York, California, and Europe. We were all there on the ranch to honor our Mama Emily.

"She'll be with us for a week, if that long. She has pneumonia and is very weak." Said Joey Jon, the family doctor.

The next day everyone was all settled in. The children played near the barn around the horses. So did I.

We were outside playing, and I was having lots of fun even though only Mama Emily could see me. I ran through the fields near the horses as if I were a child. Suddenly, a sensation came over me that stopped me in my tracks. A compelling force was pulling me into the house. When I looked up, I found myself standing in her room as she was trying to get out of bed. She heard the children playing outside and wanted to look at them.

Oh my goodness! All of my life I've loved looking out the window at nature's grace. It always gave me peace, and it does to her too. I saw that she was about to fall, so I ran over and caught her. I was certainly surprised that I could touch her at all. I was able to prevent her from falling.

"Oh my, thanks Madam." I realized she still thought I was Madam Charlotte.

She pointed toward the window and I understood that she wanted to look out the window some more. I helped her to the window to enjoy the view.

"Madam, I know you came for me, but you know that I must talk to the boys before we go," she said.

"Just take your time, I can wait," I found myself saying. "I'm not in no hurry."

I don't know why I said it like that, the words felt strange to me.

She wanted to talk more, so I took her by the arm and helped her into bed. She laughed. I forgot myself and began laughing too. I decided to talk to her like I was Madam, just to make her feel better.

"What's so funny?" I asked.

"I remember carrying you to bed by the arm when you were old and I was young," she said.

"Well it's my time to take care of you, because you were so good to me," I said affectionately.

Gazing into each other's eyes, I could see her loneliness

for the Master, and I could tell she wanted to ask me if I had seen him. Just as I was ready to tell her that I knew he was still in love with her, a cool wind came through the room and when it stopped, there he stood by the window.

He was as handsome as ever. He looked as young as he did the day that they met. She stared at him, hardly able to believe it was him. She started to cry, reaching her arms toward him. He walked right past me and swept her into his arms, hugging her with intense passion.

"Sweetheart, I've come back for you. I have been waiting so long." Emily looked into his eyes. "It's time," he said.

"Oh my darling I am ready. But first I must talk to our sons," she said. The love in his heart shone through his eyes.

Emily unexpectedly dropped off to sleep and Rosa came into the room. She seemed to sense something strange going on. She went to the window and looked out at the children. I noticed that she was checking the window as though she thought it was open. When she found it closed, she walked back to the bed near where Master was sitting.

He got up and stood nearby. Clarence Sr. came in.

"Sweetheart how is she doing?" Rosa was still looking around the room as if she could feel us.

"Baby, does it feel cold in this room now?"

He walked around the room. He almost walked right over Master.

"You know, sweetheart, it is a bit cold in here to me too, but only in certain parts of the room, like next to mother's bed."

Rosa looked at Emily. "Baby, why don't you stay here with your mother for awhile. When she wakes up, she may want to talk to you."

He pulled up a chair and sat down next to his mother's bed.

I saw Master take a seat on the edge of the bed too, so I took a seat on the other side. In just a few moments Emily opened her eyes.

"Oh sweetheart, you are still here." Clarence thought she was talking to him. He began to wonder if Rosa was right about his mother. She seemed to be slipping away.

"Mother, who are you talking to? Are you talking to me?"

"Oh, you are still here too," she said. This time she was talking to me, thinking I was Madam.

"Mother are you talking to someone else in this room too?" Her son asked.

She nodded. "Oh yes, son, don't you see Madam and the Master?"

Her son no longer had any reason to doubt his wife. He started to tell her that Rosa was coming to give her a bath, but she stopped him. She knew she was running out of time.

"Send a telegram to the others and tell them to come home," she said.

"They are already home, don't you remember?"

"Oh yes." She smiled. "Son, I am very tired, but I have something I need to say to all of my sons."

Clarence gathered his brothers, and everyone else came to pray with her. The wives, cousins, and grandchildren knew she was slipping away. All of them came immediately except Edward Leon, who made no effort to go with them.

"Edward Leon, it is her wish to see you also," Clarence said sternly. Edward Leon came along, and his son, Edward Earl started following along with them.

"No. You stay with the kids. You can come in later," said Clarence Sr.

Why is my father going if she asked for her sons only? Edward Earl wondered. He still didn't know that his father was Emily's son too.

When Emily woke up she looked right into Edward Leon's face. He asked, "Mama Emily are you cold?" She answered, "No my son." Emily was just opening her eyes again, and smiling of course. The boys thought she was smiling at them, so they smiled back. Edward Leon wondered why she called him her son.

"Come, lift up my pillow," she said, speaking to Edward Leon. "That's right. Now I can see you all better."

Emily took a large envelope from under her sheets on her

bed, handing it to Clarence Sr.

"Read this," she said. "I've grown feeble and can't speak loud enough."

He opened the document and began reading it to his brothers. It stated that they were the Master's sons, inheriting the ranch together equally after the death of their mother Emily. The ranch was not to be sold, but passed down to the children. All members of the family would pay taxes on the property once a year. Any family member not sharing in the taxes would forfeit his or her part of the inheritance.

Edward Leon was not too happy about the inheritance being equal to the others, because he felt that Hoover Ranch should belong solely to him, since he was the only living Hoover.

When Emily heard his objection, she realized that Master never told her son who he was. She knew she must tell him before she passed.

"Listen to me and listen carefully," she said. I am, and have been a Hoover for many years now. That's something I kept to myself." Then she added, "I kept it to myself because it was done for me, and for me alone."

Edward Leon said, "I knew all about that, Mama Emily, because father told me that you were my sister by a half-white colored woman." More lies.

"What else did he tell you, Edward Leon?"

"He told me that Madam Charlotte was not supposed to have any children because of her illness. So they took you from the slave women and raised you as a white girl. Now I find out that was just another one of my father's lies."

The spirit of the Master, still sitting at the edge of Emily's bed, knew he shouldn't have left this task for Emily to do or undo.

Emily reached under her sheets again and pulled out another document.

"Read it. Read it for yourself and for all your brothers."
It was a marriage certificate.

When Edward Leon saw what it was, he was outraged.

"This can't be true!" He yelled. "It's dated the day my father died."

Even the other sons didn't know about this. She said, "Edward Leon, it was the day he died, but that was my wedding day also. You were there and so were your brothers." She went on to say, "Master Edward Hoover and Madam Charlotte wanted to surprise me that day. But my sweetheart was too weak, and he had to be taken back to bed. Before he died, though, he married me."

Then she looked at her son and said, "Don't you remember Edward? Just before your father's death he signed the certificate because he wanted me to become his wife. He had never been married before. I was a Hoover then, and I am one now. Before he died he gave the marriage certificate to Sister Harriet to give to Madam. She could have burned it, but she didn't. She knew we loved each other, and she was happy for me.

"Later I told Madam to keep it because if I filed it, I thought it would cause trouble for all of us. I kept it a secret. She filed it for me anyway."

I am sure Emily didn't think things were going to happen this way. If she had only known that Master had never told Edward Leon the truth, she would have handled this differently. At that moment the pastor came in to pray for her.

"Is there anything I can do?" He asked, noticing the tension.

"No, thank you. It's a family affair, I'll handle it."

"You should wait in the other room," Edward Leon told the pastor. "This is private."

"You might want to respect a man of the cloth," admonished Emily. "God don't like ugly. You know I taught you to respect the Lord."

Her seventh son looked embarrassed.

"I didn't mean to be disrespectful, he muttered.

"Any of the rest of you have any disagreements? With my marriage or anything else?" Emily had to take a deep breath to say that, but it was important to clear the air.

No one had a problem except Edward Leon. Joey Jon had a problem with how Edward Leon was acting. She told him that Edward Leon was his real brother, and he didn't mind. He wondered why Edward Leon couldn't accept it.

"If you are a Hoover, doesn't that change all our names to Hoover?" Joey Jon asked.

"Maybe years ago it could have been done with no trouble to anyone, but it isn't feasible to change all the names now," she said.

"That is not true! You all have to go under the name of your own father and he is Old Harry Carson," Edward Leon said. Emily never liked Old Harry after she found out about Sweet Anna, so this didn't make her too happy.

"Old Harry was never the father of any of my babies," she said to Edward Leon. By this time Joey Jon had heard just about enough.

"Listen here Edward, I've had enough of your shit. You have the same father and mother we have. So sit your ass down and shut up, because I'm sick of you and your high and mighty ass."

Clarence stood up and sternly said, "Now Joey Jon that is not right. Edward doesn't know all that we know. We are all forgetting that we owe Mama Emily respect." He went on to say, "Just remember that she is ill, and we may be losing her. Tell me, is this what we want to send her away with.... a lot of hatred between her sons?"

I took one look at Master's spirit. He was proud of Clarence, just like when he was alive. I noticed that all of the boys respected Clarence. I was very quiet in the room.

Joey Jon stood up. "I'm sorry," he said to Edward Leon. Then went to the bed and sweetly kissed his mother.

"You boys are the kind of sons I'm proud of," she said. "Thank you, Clarence and Joey Jon."

"Mama Emily, maybe we should all leave the room and let you talk to Edward alone. I'm sure he needs to speak to you privately," said Clarence.

I could see that Master Hoover agreed with Clarence.

"Okay. You all come back and see me when we're finished," she said.

They all kissed her, and left the room, except Edward Leon. He went to her and laid his head on her chest. He began to sob.

He lived all of his life believing a lie. She placed her arms around his head and talked softly to him.

"Edward, I am sorry to be the one to give you pain, but I must tell you the truth. Maybe you will pass it on to your children and stop the pain, and maybe you won't. That is your choice. Just remember if you don't tell them the truth you will be doing the same thing to your children that your father did to you," she explained.

She looked into his eyes. Even at her age, her eyes shone with a gentle light. She went on talking, "I want you to listen to me. First of all, I am your natural mother which means you came from my body. Master Hoover is your father. He is the only man that I have ever had from the age of twenty. He is the father of all seven of my sons. You were my seventh son. He picked you out over all the others because he wanted you to carry his name into the future, to be raised as a white child. He loved all of his sons, but I think he loved you more, and you should be proud."

"Why did he love me more?" He asked.

"Master felt that you were the best gift that he could have given to Madam because he couldn't give her his love. So, he gave her our love, and that was you." She answered.

He was surprised at that answer.

She went on to say, "You didn't look any whiter than the others. You were born on a special day. Madam Charlotte's birthday".

"Now, when I told your brothers he didn't give them his last name, they were angry with him, and very disappointed too. Most of all they felt that they were different. Despite that, I taught them to be proud of the fact that they were getting a chance in life. I told them that lots of slaves were beaten and hungry, but we were not, and it was because of the Master. You don't know what its like being a slave."

Emily rarely talked about it, but she told him how hard it was for her, growing up as a slave before Master bought her.

She went on to say, "I was born a slave, but when Master brought me home from that slave auction and took me to the arms of Madam Charlotte, it was then, and only then, that my life was worth living."

The spirit of the Master looked as though he was weeping, sitting there at the end of the bed.

Edward Leon raised his head and looked into his mother's face, with his eyes full of tears.

"Did Madam Charlotte love you too?" He asked.

"Yes son, she did; she took me in her arms, protected me, and raised me like I was her own child. She protected me from all men and she taught me everything I knew. Most of all she taught me how to love. When I turned twenty years old she turned me over to Master because she knew he was in love with me from the beginning."

Her son was starting to feel better about things, and he began to understand what it was like being born a slave.

"You know, Edward, I wanted to have even more babies after you were born," she confessed.

"Why didn't you?" He asked.

"Well, Master just got too old, or maybe God just felt seven was enough. All my boys were conceived in love and passion. We both knew that our love was forever, and I know he still loves me even now." She looked at his spirit sitting there on the edge of the bed smiling at her, waiting to take her away with him forever.

I could see that she was getting weaker and weaker.

"Son, don't hate your father and me. You boys were our joy. When he asked me to let you carry his last name and wanted you to be raised as a white child, it made me proud. Edward, the memory you had of your father before today was good, so keep it. God has forgiven him. And now, son, I am asking you to forgive us both."

"There is nothing to forgive. You were always a good

mother, even though I was told you were my nanny. I just want to know one more thing," he said. "What did Madam Charlotte do all of those years without a man, during the time her husband was sleeping with a slave girl and having seven children with her?"

"Their marriage was what you call a forced marriage. Madam was in love with another man."

"Yes, but she didn't go off and sleep with him."

"Son, whatever Madam did, it is not up to us to judge. I know that she asked God for forgiveness for her sins before she died. It is true that Joel Edward might have been her lover's son."

"I am telling you to stop the secrets that have caused so much pain in all of our lives. I am trying not to keep secrets from you anymore," she said.

She went on to say, "So you see son, things are not always what they seem."

She closed her eyes again, but this time she didn't open them anymore. The end had come, and her spirit began to leave her body as I stood there watching.

The door opened and it was all of the boys and their wives. I looked in the corner of the room by the window, and was surprised to see the spirits of Emily's three dead sons. They were standing there, waiting for her too.

"Hello boys, you came for me too?" She spoke softly. Only the spirits could hear her. Master stood waiting with his arms folded. It was very romantic, the way he sat there waiting for her soul to leave her body to come with him.

A glow came over her. Her spirit became younger. She looked like she did the day of her coming out party.

I looked at Master as he stood up like he was getting ready to leave. They took each other's hands and started toward the window, along with their three sons, and Madam Charlotte who was leaving my body. I followed them through the window, and noticed all the others; Ms. Lilly, Willie, Old Harry, Sweet Anna, Percy Carson, Dr. Pitts, and the others. It looked like they were all there to celebrate Mama Emily going home.

"She is gone now," the doctor was saying.

He covered her face. I watched until I couldn't see them any longer. They vanished into a beautiful white flash into the clouds. Edward Leon came to terms with the news, but he wasn't sure of what to do next.

"I am in a spot with my wife and her parents, they won't understand if I tell them I'm a colored man. They are prejudiced against colored people, and all this time they thought I was white, and so did I. What do you think I should do?" He asked his brothers.

"Leave it be, don't tell anyone anything different," they advised.

I could see the relief on his face. A heavy burden was lifted from him when he made the decision to pass for white forever. The deceit goes on.

11

I turned to go back into the house but felt very tired and sleepy. I noticed it was late. There sat the carriage, so I climbed into the back just to take a nap. I fell into a deep sleep immediately. Apparently only for seconds. I soon heard laughter and music, and was soon awakened.

I realized that I was still in back of the carriage, so I sat up and looked out. I found myself alone in front of the saloon. Everything looked different. I realized it was the Christmas decorations. I could hear the most beautiful sounds of Christmas, and a group of colored people caroling. "I didn't know they did that back in the 1800s," I thought.

Everyone was beautifully dressed in holiday colors, and joyously singing. I heard an amazing voice.

"I know that voice. That beautiful voice!" I thought. I looked out of the carriage and it was Sister Harriet. I loved to hear her sing, so I just sat for awhile and enjoyed the music. Around her stood a group of children who sang like nothing I'd ever heard or seen in my world.

I must have nearly drifted off to sleep again, because time sped. I noticed things were different. I saw a sign in front of the saloon that read:

"The 1895 HOOVER & ALLEN Holiday Gala"

The festive streets were filled with people dressed in holiday fashions. I wanted to look pretty too, so I closed my eyes and made a wish. When I opened my eyes, I was dressed up, and I looked stunning, if I do say so myself.

The dress that I was wearing was velvet, and my favorite color, green. I even wore makeup, and my hair was in an up-do. It made me feel like a queen. I started to climb out of the carriage and just as I put one foot on the ground, I felt a hand. I was shocked that someone could see me and touch me. I could feel it. How strange.

I heard a voice speaking to me. I was afraid. How could they see me? When I got both feet on the ground, I turned to see who had my arm. He was a good-looking, half-white gentleman. I could tell he was colored by his beautiful lips and nice curly hair.

"Are you lost?" He said.

I didn't know what to do or say. I stood speechless, but I knew that he could tell I was lost.

"You must be looking for the Hoover and Allen gala. It's at the Mid Town Saloon."

I didn't know how to respond so I walked a little further trying to regain my composure. I couldn't help but turn to him again, though.

"Yes, I am sir! I am lost!"

"Where do you come from?" He asked.

I could tell he was very intelligent and he was charmingly polite. He must be an Allen, I thought.

"I live across the river sir," I said, deciding I'd have to make it up as I go.

"May I escort you to the door?"

Something about him made me feel elegant. Like royalty, I extended my hand, yet I wondered who he was.

"Sir, and what might be your name?"

He looked at me for a moment, a smile playing at the edges of his lips.

"My name is Peter Joe Allen madam, and who might you be?"

I didn't know what to do then, so I came up with another name. How could I tell him I was an Allen? He'd wonder why he didn't know me, if I was family.

"My name is Ruby Dee, sir."

This seemed to satisfy him. Arm in arm, we walked to the Mid Town Saloon where a party was going strong. He opened the door for me. I held Peter Joe's arm as he ushered me in. The saloon was adorned with festive holiday decorations. Dinner tables were arranged around the room. I was almost giddy as the spirit of the holiday surrounded me, with everyone laughing, dancing, and having a good time. And everywhere, I realized, were my own relatives. "I really am a part of the past," I thought, and began to relax. Peter put his lips close to my ear and said,

"Uncle Clarence Sr. rented the saloon for the family party." The Hoovers started this Christmas celebration many years past. Since Master Hoover and Joel Edward Hoover have passed away, Clarence Allen Sr. continues the tradition."

I looked around the room and saw Clarence Jr. and his wife Cora carrying a new baby. I believed that baby was my "Big Daddy."

I cannot tell you how wonderful it felt to actually be part of this celebration with my ancestors. It made me feel so very special. I was happy, but then I realized a terrible truth.

"It must be 1895," I thought. "That's around the time my Big Daddy was a child." I was the only one at the party from the future that knew about a terrible truth that was going to happen to the family in the year 1895.

When I looked at Big Daddy's mother across the room I remembered that night when she went with him on the moonlight ride. I looked around the room to see who else was still alive and who was attending this event. I was excited and I knew that I needed to relax because I wanted to enjoy myself. Everyone could see me now, or so I thought.

No one really paid any attention to Peter Joe and I standing there at the door, except for one cousin who smiled and said hello to him. A few minutes into the party, I let go of his arm while one of his cousins, whom he called Charlotte, began speaking to him. She took him by the arm just as though I wasn't even there.

"Come on, Peter, let's go see the others." I was left standing there alone. She sure didn't notice me. I think Peter Joe forgot about me as he wandered off with her. Charlotte was very pretty and just as kind as her grandmother, Madam Charlotte.

I felt lonely, so I decided to mingle. I set out to find out who was attending this party. I saw our host, Clarence Sr., and his wife, my great-great-grandmother Rosa. They were sitting together in a lounging chair talking. She was every bit of 81 years old. She was still so pretty. They were holding hands. "It seems that the Allen boys were romantic," I thought.

Well, maybe the women who married Allen men were pretty, but if I must say so myself, the Allen boys were the best looking men I'd had seen so far.

I saw Edward Earl and his prejudiced wife, Carol Lynn, from Washington D.C. whom no one liked. They brought their five-year-old son, John Edward to the gala.

Uncle Edward Earl's father, Edward Leon Hoover, was also in attendance with his wife, Aunt Sheila Mae. Edward Leon worked at the Pentagon in Washington D.C., just like his son.

My favorite cousin already, was certainly Peter Joe. His parents, Uncle Evan Lee and his wife Elaine, were both at the party.

After the death of Joel Edward, Aunt Eva remarried. Her daughter, named after Madam Charlotte, was attending the gala with her mother and stepfather Mr. Fred Piece. They moved around a lot because of his job. At this time they were living in New York, but they kept in touch with the family often and weren't about to miss the party.

Despite secrets and deceit, the Hoover and Allen families remained close for many years. And my New York relatives weren't the ones that traveled the greatest distance to attend. Aunt Betty Jane brought Little Lilly home for Christmas, all the way from Europe.

Her name was about all Little Lilly had in common with Ms. Lilly. Her character left a lot to be desired. She was very pushy and bossy and loved to start trouble.

Little Lilly was nothing like Ms. Lilly, who cooked, kept house, and cared for the family for many years. Miss Lilly had passed away, but everyone called her their "Big Mama" at one time or another. Everyone loved Miss Lilly, and at the end of her life they took especially good care of her.

It was said that when Miss Lilly lost Willie, it seemed as though she gave up. I will always remember her talks with Emily. When she talked about Willie, she'd say, "I loved that man."

I really missed seeing Master Hoover, Madam Charlotte, Emily, Miss Lilly, Old Harry, Willie, Sweet Anna, old Master Montgomery who was Madam Charlotte's brother, and Dr. Pitts. All were dead now. It was sad.

Also attending the party, were Uncle Joey Jon Allen, his lovely wife, Jacqueline. I felt proud that he was a doctor. The first doctor in the family. They brought their two children with them. David Roy and Emily.

Getting used to the new generation was difficult. I missed seeing the excitement of Emily and Master Hoover's electrifying romantic sexual encounters. Loving each other deeply, they carried secrets and deceit to the grave.

My ancestors socialized together in groups; all the young people stuck together, laughing and having fun. Wanting to have some fun too, I decided to walk over to see what was making my cousins laugh. I felt like I knew them already. I also wanted to see if I could recognize cousins, aunts, and uncles that I'd meet living in the future.

"Peter Joe!" I called out to him, but I don't think he heard me.

So, I walked closer. They were laughing at Peter Joe for some reason. He looked sad.

"Peter Joe, I think you really need to tell your parents about your hallucinations," Lilly said, with her characteristic lack of tact.

Charlotte stepped up. "Shut up Lilly, you don't know what you are talking about. Come on Peter Joe." She took him by the arm and started walking away with him. That made Lilly angry, and she shouted,

"You shut up yourself Charlotte Hoover. You're just taking his side because you have a thing for him."

The blushing Charlotte stopped walking and looked at Lilly angrily. She was embarrassed. Peter Joe was rather surprised. Charlotte walked right up and stood in Lilly's face. She could no longer hold her tongue.

"Peter Joe is my cousin and you don't deserve to be named after Ms.Lilly. You are nothing like her. She was a much better person than you, and you'll never be like her!"

Wow! I looked over to see what was going on with their parents. The mothers were coming our way. When Charlotte finished talking to Lilly everyone looked shocked, and so did I.

A parent spoke, "Don't talk to each other like that!" It wasn't just a fight they were concerned about. With the thoughtless way the children were talking, they worried that someone might slip and blurt out a family secret right in front of the guests.

"Don't gossip about what goes on in the family," they admonished. The mothers hovered around, but the fathers went back to their corners and continued their drinking, laughing, and telling jokes about their sex lives. It was understood that it was the mother's job to keep the children in line.

For instance, I listened to Aunt Carol Lynn talk to her five-year-old son John Edward. I don't think I'll ever forget that conversation. She took him into a corner and said quietly, "John Edward, you listen to me, don't get involved in any of that "nigger" talk. We are here only out of respect to your white side of the family. You and Charlotte are the only children here that are pure white. No nigger blood in you."

John Edward said, "But they are my cousins, they aren't niggers."

"You'll understand better when you're older," she said.

"They look white like me," said John Edward, looking confused.

"When we get back to Washington, we'll have a talk about what a nigger is," said Aunt Carol Lynn.

Aunt Carol had no idea that she was married to a man with colored blood. Her husband Edward Earl didn't even know the secret himself because his father never told him. Even his father, Emily's seventh son Edward Leon, didn't know it himself until he was a grown man. He couldn't tell his family. By the time he found out himself, he was already married to a white woman. Her family was prejudiced against colored people. Therefore, the lie he lived was passed down to his only son Edward Earl Hoover, who was now going to be passing it down to his only son John Edward.

It was a hard decision, but Edward Leon planned to tell everyone at the family's gala. He was getting up in age and he felt it was time for them to know.

I looked across the room, and noticed he was all alone. He walked away from his brothers, and was standing in front of a window in deep thought. I walked over to him hoping that I would be able to speak to him, wanting to see if he would notice me. Maybe I could make him feel better. I felt sad for him. Just as I got ready to speak to him his brother Joey Jon walked up.

"Hey brother Edward, what's going on with you? Is everything all right?"

He looked at his brother with eyes full of pain.

"I'm in turmoil inside, and I don't know how much longer I can keep living this lie." They took a seat at one of the tables to talk.

Clarence Sr., was now growing old in age, was talking to his brother Evan Lee, who was also up in age. Edward Leon looked older than both of them even though he was younger. It was said that he looked older because of the stress of hiding the truth for so many years.

He felt that he couldn't tell the truth about his bloodline, because he thought he would lose everything he loved, and worked for all those years. In the capitol of the United States, you didn't get good government positions if you were of mixed blood.

Clarence Sr. and Evan Lee finally joined them. Emily prayed that all of the brothers would remained friends, and they did, until they all died.

The brothers were ready to free Edward Leon's mind of his fears. Brother Evan Lee stated,

"You don't need to worry about family secrets, because it's all safe. Master already protected us, and our secrets, in every way possible." They reassured him.

"Edward, your life is safe with us. Our father was 'The Master of Deceit' and we know how to keep a secret. We love you, and we'll protect you forever. Your secret is safe with us. Go on living just as you have. You are a white man, and that is the way it's going to stay," said Clarence Sr.

All of the brothers came to a decision to meet with all of their sons and tell them the truth. They would tell only their sons because they were sure that the men of the family would honor the family secret.

We were having fun at the party. I was reminiscing a lot about family history, and I was learning a lot more about my heritage and ethnicity so that when I went home it would be a good story to tell.

It was still 1895. I found myself going in all different directions. It was interesting to get to know the Hoovers from Washington D.C.

Still at the gala, but moving through time so fast. I couldn't stop it. I don't think I want to anyway.

While back in time, I remember looking at a hand-written book in the family library. It stated that three of Master Hoover's sons were registered in records in the town hall in Mississippi.

The book also said that the Allens were relatives of the Hoovers. Though this was my fantasy, traveling back in time, the information seemed very specific. Later, I would find out what the records would show in my own time era, but here the Allen boys were listed like this:

*Clarence Allen Sr.

Son of Emily Allen, a white woman born 1793.

A relative of Master Edward D. Hoover

That was the way Master Hoover protected them all. All of Emily's sons were listed this way. All of the sons born by

Emily were named Allen, except one. Edward Leon was registered in the town hall of records with the name Hoover.

Although slavery ceased in 1865, the Hoovers and the Allens still ran Hoover Ranch. In 1889, after Mama Emily passed away, the Allen boys inherited the ranch along with the only living Hoover son, Edward Leon, who was also born of Emily while she was a slave.

After the big 1895 holiday gala, lots of changes were made with regard to the future of Hoover Ranch. When Edward Leon returned to Washington, he realized that his life was in good hands with his Mississippi family. They would protect his secret. It was safe for him to continue living as a white man.

Later, his son, Edward Earl, found out that his grandfather was really the seventh son of a slave girl. He had known his real grandmother all his life, since she was a nanny for the Hoovers. Even though he loved her when he was a little boy, he was surprised at first and didn't want to believe it. In his heart, discovering that he had a drop of colored blood, hurt him.

"I'm not going to change now after twenty years as a white man," he said to his father. "I don't want to learn how to be a colored man! What do you think will happen to my career with the government in Washington, D.C. if this gets out?"

He was right, of course. In those times the "one drop" rule was how it worked. One drop of colored blood meant you were classified as colored, and colored people weren't appointed to high positions, period.

Edward Earl's father, Edward Leon, trusted and loved his brothers, but Edward Earl never did care for his uncles in Mississippi. By the time he was fifty years old, he wanted to make a few changes. He didn't trust the Allens, and he wasn't sure his great-grandfather's master plan would protect him adequately.

"Nobody's threatening you," his father said.

Nothing could change the fact that he saw colored people still oppressed. He knew exactly what would happen to a mulatto man who was passing for white. He thought, The man would lose everything, and possibly his life.

No one wanted to hurt him, but he believed that the secret gave the Allens the power to control his family if they chose to. He figured it was time to separate the lives of his family from the Allens because he thought problems might flare up in the future.

After all this, I found myself in deep thought about the way the Hoover's in Washington D.C., felt later in life. Remembering, I realize that what my Big Daddy told me was true.

Edward Earl, his wife Carol Lynn, and their son John Edward never visited the Allens again after the 1895 gala.

He and his family wanted to move into politics and into higher positions in Washington, D.C. They realized that if the family were caught socializing with niggers this chance would be gone. Worse, he didn't want anyone to blackmail him with a story about him having colored bloodline. He had to think of a way to separate the Allens from the Hoovers, for good.

He realized that he could blackmail them into keeping their mouths shut. First, he had to tell his wife a lie, so that neither she nor any of their children would know the secret. This is the lie that he told his wife:

"The Allens took my inheritance of the family ranch in Mississippi," he said. Carol Lynn was shocked, but what he said next really angered her. "As if that wasn't enough, now they are trying to say that I have colored blood in my veins!"

"Don't make up details, tell only what you need," was what Master Hoover had told Miss Lilly many years ago. He must have inherited some of his thinking from the Master of Deceit, because in a round about way, he actually told his wife the truth. It worked. They both cut the Allen's right out of their lives.

But that wasn't enough for him. He knew he had to work out a master plan to get rid of the Allens forever. He settled on the idea of making a contract with them. Without anyone else knowing, he contacted Clarence.

"If you don't sign this, your whole family could be killed, one by one," he said. "And Mr. Allen, you got my word on that." The contract stated:

#1 The Allens would keep complete silence about the colored blood that ran through the veins of any Hoover.

#2 The Allens would not contact the Hoovers in the future as relatives for any reason. Any contact would be about business only.

#3 Any Allen upon request could use the Hoover influence in Washington D.C., to enhance the careers of any member of the Allen family.

"But all of the requests must be within our power. In exchange for our help with your careers, we require complete silence about our family ties. Mind you, the secret must be kept forever. If any member of the Allens violates the contract by divulging the family secret, we'll do whatever it takes to protect ourselves," he said.

He elaborated on the rules to make sure they were crystal clear. "Now we enter into this agreement knowing all the rules." The Hoovers would use their power to rid themselves of anyone that threatens them.

By signing this contract, the Hoovers thought they would be free from the Allens forever. They gave all rights to the Hoover Ranch Plantation to the Allens.

Years later John Edward reinforced the contract by saying,

"This is not just for my family, it's for all of us, the Allens and the Hoovers. We must keep father's secrets forever."

"This is a political decision," John Edward Hoover told Clarence Allen III.

Edward Leon died, Emily's son who passed for white. His son, Edward Earl and grandson, John Edward, took over running things. By this time, they knew that John Edward's career was rising. They were glad the family secret would not hurt his growing access to power. By this time, all of the Mississippi Hoovers had migrated to Washington, D.C., with the sole exception of Charlotte Hoover, the daughter of the late

Joel Edward Hoover. Young Charlotte moved to Beverly Hills, California and married a colored man. She was actually the only pure white Hoover, and she married a colored man.

In Washington D.C., Edward Earl had a heart full of anger directed toward his grandparents. He never thought that slaves should have been given equal shares of the ranch. Even though his father was just as colored as any of the Allen brothers, he thought the whole business was just plain wrong.

"If it meant giving up the plantation to them, it was worth it. They are out of our lives now," he said to his wife.

John Edward made up a new story, just in case he needed it. He told everyone that Emily Allen was Master Hoover's sister who died in the 1800s. This was another lie. I found John Edward to be even more deceitful than the old man Hoover.

John Edward entered law school, and while he was there he had trouble trying to fit in with the girls. The colored blood in his veins haunted him. He was afraid to fall in love. What would happen if he produced a dark-skinned child? Being colored meant that something was wrong with you in the brain. That's what his mother taught him. Both parents taught him to hate colored people.

"They are intelligent," he told himself. When he was in grade school, he learned a lot about genes, and how they affect the way children look and act. He also learned that a child could be born with features of ancestors. Genes could reach back many generations. If he ever got married, he knew the family secret might get out. That was something he didn't want to happen.

When John Edward thought about his life, filled with secrets that came from the body of a slave girl, it always made him unhappy. He found himself hating all colored people, because they reminded him of something he could not accept. He could not even look at one. It became hard for him to talk to a colored person without feeling anger. He found himself with a disease I called," *Psychosis of Racism.*" He hated himself.

Later, when people started to ask why he never married,

he started a rumor that he was gay, just because he didn't want to become a father. It was something he came to fear, knowing that the child's looks might tell the family secret. If he wanted to be with a woman it would be in secret, and the Hoovers had practiced keeping secrets for at least five generations.

When John Edward graduated, he took a job as a clerk in the Justice Department. After receiving his degree in law, he very quickly became the assistant to the Attorney General. He used this position to help Emily's sons get better jobs in the government as white men. This was his way of blackmailing the Allens into keeping his great-grandfather's secret. He didn't know that Emily, and all her kin, believed in keeping secrets when they were asked to. He was never in any danger of being exposed by them.

I closed my eyes and I went backward again, just for a moment. When I opened them, I was back at the gala in 1895. I stood there feeling badly for little John Edward. He was taught to hate by his own mother. It appeared to me as a child, he wanted to love his cousins. Through his eyes at that time, he saw no difference.

His mother, Carol, was another matter. She'd already learned to hate when she was a child. She was very prejudiced. I stood there watching Carol and I thought she was a very unhappy person. She had so much hate in her heart, it made her look ugly.

This explains why John Edward grew up with so much hate in his heart toward colored people. They told John Edward as he was growing up that the Allens were colored slaves owned by the Hoovers. He was told that Master Hoover committed a sin by having children with Emily Allen, a colored slave. His father Edward Earl told him that the Allens stole his inheritance. This went way back. It was said that when Edward Leon was a child they would overhear him telling Joel Edward, that Emily's colored boys were going to take everything.

"Emily's children are our cousins, and they are just as

equal as we are," Joel Edward would say. This made Edward Leon angry. He even called Joel a nigger lover. That didn't matter to Joel because he loved all of his cousins. He thought Edward Leon was just blowing off steam, but he wasn't. He grew up hating all of the boys. He even hated his white brother for not taking his side against the Allen boys, until he found out the truth. One of the guards from the big house told Clarence Sr. that after the Civil War Edward Leon said he was glad that Joel was killed in the war.

"He got what he deserved for loving niggers," he said.

"Well then, why do you love Emily so much?" The guard asked.

His answer showed that he felt pretty confused. "Emily is my sister so that makes her different. She takes care of me." That was how Emily's life fit into their lives, in his mind.

Well, when I collected my thoughts, I went back to the party. I started mingling again, looked across the room and spotted Peter Joe. I wondered why he was sitting there looking so unhappy. I decided to go over and cheer him up. I had taken a liking to him because he looked so much like my son Vincent. Now I had an idea of what Vincent was going to look like when he grew up.

I walked over and sat down next to him.

"Hello beautiful where have you been?" He asked.

Just as I sat down with him, cousin Charlotte walked up.

"Peter Joe why are you sitting here talking to yourself?"

I realized that for some reason, he was able to see me, but no one else could. All evening, we thought everyone could see me. I thought they were not talking to me because I was a stranger.

He looked at me and he remembered how I had just appeared, hanging on to the carriage. One minute I wasn't there, and the next minute I was right in front of him.

"You know, you just popped in front of me like a ghost. Are you a figment of my imagination?" Peter Joe was really looking worried. "Maybe I am loony," he said.

I felt so sad. Trying to cheer him up made things worse.

I wanted to do something to make it up to him, but didn't know what. I looked up, and all the kids were running towards us.

Little Lilly spoke up. "I was right Charlotte! You should stop taking up for him and stay away from that loony." Laughing, they all walked away, dragging Charlotte by the hand.

Peter Joe got up and ran out on the terrace of the saloon. He was hurt and sad. I followed him out.

"Get away from me, I'm bad news can't you see? I'm loony."

"No, you are not a loony. You are brighter than any one of them," I said.

"I wish that were true, then they would have to apologize to me for all the times that they hurt me."

"Peter Joe, my name is not Ruby Dee; I am your cousin from the future and I was born in 1947. In your time, I would not have been born yet!"

He stared at me. "You know, I believe you. But they are never going to believe that."

"No, they won't believe it, and you are not going to tell them about me," I said.

"Well, how am I ever going to get them to like me?" He asked.

"We'll think of something to do together." I said.

Despite the problems, he was excited about meeting me. He wanted to know if I knew what his life was going to be like, and how long he was going to live? I told him that I did, but I was not going to tell him.

"Telling you would be bad luck. No one should try to change the future or alter any part of the past," I said.

"We should just try to make our futures better by trying to make a difference," he said.

I was so proud of him. Then I knew why he was able to see me, and no one else could. It was because he was special.

"Okay, I will tell you a little about your future," I said. "You will live a long, good life. Many people like you, though you don't realize it right now."

Feeling better, we started thinking of a way to change his cousins' minds about him. All at once he turned and looked at me. He had an idea and I had one too.

"Okay, you go first!" I said.

"If you could fly, I could tell them that I have magic powers," he said.

"Well, I can't fly and I don't think that's a good idea, because I'm not sure what I could do if I could fly."

"Well, what is your idea?" He asked.

"I'm trying to think of something to make your cousins believe in you." I could see that made him happy.

"Well how can you do that?" He said.

"I know something no one else knows. It will happen in your future, and it may not be good. But you can tell it to them before it happens and when it does happen they'll think you have great powers, and that you can predict the future," I said.

He thought that was a great idea.

"Now," I said, "they are not going to believe you until it happens, but don't worry about that. When it really happens they will respect you forever."

He got so excited, he hugged me. He seemed surprised that he could feel me, and no one else could see or hear me. He was very impatient. He was holding me tight.

"Let go, so that I can think of something to tell you." I thought for a moment. Then I said, "This is the only thing I can think of but it is not good news. As a matter of fact it's down right awful, and very sad."

"Oh my! What?" He was excited, but after thinking about it I didn't want to tell him. "Please, I've got to know. Please, tell me, even if it's awful. It's got to be something big, to get their attention."

"I hope he doesn't think he can change this or try to stop it from happening," I was thinking.

"Nothing can ever be changed, altered or stopped because it has already happened in the future," I explained.

That didn't change his mind.

"What is the awful tragedy that is going to strike and

change many lives?" He asked, starting to get impatient.

"Okay! Remember, I didn't want to tell you. In 1895, Uncle Clarence Allen Jr. will be killed by outlaws in town, but I don't know when or where."

He stared at me. "Oh! My God! This is 1895."

I felt terrible. How could I be so insensitive? I totally forgot that Clarence Jr. was his favorite uncle. He was heartbroken. He started crying and ran into the other room repeating, "That's not true, that can't be true."

When he entered the party in tears, shouting those words, the party stopped. His uncle Clarence Jr. had left a short time ago with two men. They had come into the saloon telling him about a man in town who was looking for him. The man was angry about the last card game that they'd played together. The man had lost his life savings to Clarence and said he felt cheated. He was accusing him of stacking the deck.

Evan Lee heard Peter Joe crying. He and Aunt Elaine ran over to their son.

"What's wrong son?" They asked.

The whole family had fear in their eyes. It wasn't like him to become emotional like this.

"Father, Uncle Clarence will be killed tonight." His father held him close after he looked into his eyes. He could tell that his son was frightened and that it was real. I was so sorry that I told him. I knew now it was the wrong thing to do. The whole family thought that he must be ill and they were all very concerned about him.

"Who told you that awful lie? Was it Little Lilly?"

He stopped them from going after Lilly. "No. It's just something I know, from inside of my heart."

His father, and mother were getting ready to take him home when they heard a loud sound outside in the streets. Alarmed, all the men got together and went to see if anything had happened. While they were gathering to go out, Clarence Sr. noticed that his son wasn't back in the saloon.

"He went down the street with a couple of friends earlier, but he hadn't returned," said Joel Jon.

Peter Joe and the other older kids had to stay inside the saloon with the ladies, while the men went to check out the loud noise down the street.

I felt so bad. I walked over to him and he grabbed my hand.

"I'm going to go and see what happened, since no one can see me," I said. "I'll be right back with some information."

He was holding my hand so tight. "Please don't leave me," he begged.

His mother was sitting with him and thought he was talking to her. "I am not going to leave you Peter Joe," she answered.

Then I said, "Peter Joe, I am not leaving you, I will always be with you." He let go of my hand.

I ran out the door passing up the men so I could get there first.

Oh my goodness! It was Clarence Jr., but it was too late. He was already dead. I watched the men trying to help him, but they couldn't bring him back. I turned and ran back to the saloon to tell Peter Joe.

When I got back the party had stopped. Everyone was sitting with him and Aunt Cora. Suddenly she was a widow, but didn't know it. She was holding her three-week-old son. "My Big Daddy someday," I thought. He had just lost his father, who was only 29 years old, and he would never get a chance to know him.

Little Lilly, Charlotte, all the other cousins, and friends walked over to Peter Joe when I returned. He looked into my eyes and got up right away, moving closer to Aunt Cora and the baby. He put his arms around her and sat down. No one spoke.

Clarence Jr. lay dead on the ground in a puddle of blood, shot in the head and stomach. Of all the memories coming back to me, this was one I'd wished that I didn't have.

Everyone noticed Peter Joe as he looked up toward the door where I was standing. They couldn't see my tears.

"He can't be dead - shot in the head and stomach - who shot him?" Peter Joe was beside himself with grief.

Aunt Cora looked at him. "Who's shot in the head and stomach Peter Joe?" She said.

All the kids stared at him with respect; they no longer believed he was loony.

Meanwhile the men found Clarence down the street alone. Lying face down dead, with blood running out the sides of his mouth. His father, Clarence Sr., was kneeling, devastated. He picked up his dead son's head and put it in his lap and cried like a baby as he held him.

The men helped carry the body to a carriage brought over to take the body to the coroner's office. They walked back to the saloon with his father.

"Why my son, why not me?" Said Clarence Sr. When they walked through the door, his wife Rosa was already crying, unable to comprehend that her son was dead. So was everyone else. As the men came in, they wondered if something else had happened, because no one had come back to tell them about the shooting.

"What happened?" Evan Lee asked.

"Peter Joe told us," said Lilly.

"And how did he find out?" Peter Joe stood up.

"I got a feeling in my heart, then a spirit told me," he said.

Only two weeks before Christmas, the tragedy caused such pain to the family. The celebration was over.

"A death before Christmas. That's pretty sad," said one of the guests. That was exactly what I was thinking.

Soon we were all on our way back to Hoover Ranch with Aunt Cora, trying to comfort her. I found myself crying, because that baby was my Big Daddy. I got into the carriage with Peter Joe and rode with them. When we arrived at the ranch, Charlotte and Lilly wanted to help take care of the baby. So did I, but nobody could see me except Peter Joe.

Aunt Cora was so upset.

"My son will never know his father," she said, starting to cry. Peter Joe hugged her. All family members stayed with her and the baby until she was exhausted and fell asleep.

This Christmas celebration, which began in such special

delight for me, had ended in deep sadness. Complete silence reigned throughout the house.

When we arrived, I noticed that the ranch looked different to me. It had been rebuilt with real lights and a new fence around it. When we arrived inside the house, I felt so sad that I decided that it was time for me to go back home. I got up to leave. Peter Joe must have seen me leaving and ran after me. When I turned and started walking away, the next thing that I knew, he had me by the arm. He wanted to talk to me and said, "Thanks Ruby Dee, and please don't be sad because you told me what was going to happen. It's not your fault and it did help me." He went on to say, "You see, everyone looks up to me and believes in me now."

I was happy about that, but I had to go home now.

I felt sleepy and I knew it was time to go. I started to fade in and out of Peter Joe's sight. I heard him calling for me, and I opened my eyes for a moment.

"Please don't leave me, you promised me you'd never leave me!"

"Peter Joe, I told you that I'll always be with you in spirit, and I will, but I need to leave now or I will die in the future. We can't change the future." I now wanted to live more than ever, and I had a strong reason for it.

"I need to tell my family the story about all of you. I love you, Peter Joe," I said hurriedly. Then, I vanished.

The mystery man, Ivery Hoover.
November 24, 1859 - November 18, 1917

My Roots,
My Life!

Author Millie L. McGhee

Meet My Family,
The People I Love...

Author's parents,
Rev. William McGhee and Alberta Allen McGhee.

*Mother, Alberta
McGhee at 18*

*First Child,
Queen Ester*

In Memory of Eddis Marie McGhee

Eddis Marie

*Dad and Mom with deceased
sister Eddis Marie.*

Mom and Eddis

*Best friends
Cherie Stewart and Millie.*

Author at age 10.

Big Daddy was Seven feet tall, so I thought. He'd lean against the railing on the porch and told me stories about the family. That's Big Daddy in the background. I'm in the front, middle, with my brother, and sister.

Queen, Bill, and Millie.

Author, Millie McGhee in Government Projects at age 16.

Nine of the McGhee's in the Government Projects. R-L: Bill, Queen, Mom, Eddis, Doug, Bobby, Lydia, Sylvia, and Jeannette.

"What I liked most about Christmas was the dolls, a black doll and a white doll." - Millie McGhee
"Those dolls represent People, all different, but yet the same." - Reverend W. M. McGhee

Four of six McGhee Sisters

Queen and Millie, best friends.

Little sisters Sylvia and Jeannette.

50 Year Wedding Anniversary

Reverend William and Alberta McGhee. Parents of eight children living today.

Parents and Children Today

*Mom and Dad with the five girls, (Left)
Queen, Millie, Lydia, Sylvia, and Jeannette.*

*Mom and Dad with all eight children, and the
boys including, (Left) Bill, Doug, and Bobby.*

Granddad and Big Daddy.
"Dreams do Come True!"
Look at me now.

From the Government Projects in McComb, Mississippi
illiterate, now a successful author, and CEO.

Living in her dream house today in Rancho Cucamonga,
California.

Special Thanks!

"My mentor and God Father Johnnie L. Cochran Sr. Dear Daddy Cochran, It's easy to take things for granted. We assume that you know the things never said somehow, but I'm happy I had the opportunity to tell you how much I love you. It's so easy to be proud of you, because you are my hero. Thanks for being there for me always. I love you!"

- Millie L. McGhee.

Author's Family!

*Wedding day. Married eleven years.
Author and husband, Leslie L.
Morris.*

*Author with family, Husband Leslie,
Son Vincent, Daughter Kym, and
Granddaughter Tyara.*

Granddaughter, Tyara Reed. Seven Years Old.

Final Research Trip
New Orleans & Mississippi

Arriving in McComb, Mississippi April 10, 2002
Our first day reviewing the research.
Denise, Lucius, Danny, Kristy, Leslie, Millie, Mertine,
Regina, Haley, and Queen. Mother stayed in the limousine.

We traveled in two limousines carrying fourteen people.
Many thanks to Lee Jennings Enterprises Inc.!

Author, Millie L. McGhee in New Orleans.

(Cookie) Denise Bouldin enjoying this trip viewing the research and shopping. Thanks to Charles, our driver.

Danny Arguello, Vice President of Allen Morris Publishing. His second trip to Mississippi.

The author in the lobby of the Days Inn.
McComb, Mississippi.

Mother, Alberta McGhee on her second research trip back
home with her "stylish" glasses!

A Dream Come True.

Author's first time in city hall at age fifty four.

Viewing history in McComb City Hall.

Colonel Henry Simpson McComb, Mayor of
McComb, Mississippi.
This was a very interesting find. America's History!
Emily Allen was impregnated by Eff McComb.
Could this be a relative?

Mayor J.C. Woods of McComb, Mississippi presenting the Author a Certificate of Appreciation with childhood friend and Administrator Jacqueline Martin.

Author, Millie L. McGhee and Cousin Kristy Hoover Sullivan meeting with the Mayor, J.C. Woods.

Haley Sullivan traveling with Mother, Kristy Hoover Sullivan at City Hall, and enjoying the trip.

Author's Sister Queen E. McGhee Tobias returned home after many years excited about the visit to City Hall with child-hood friend, Regina Johnson.

A talk with Mayor J.C. Woods while at City Hall.

Leaving City Hall. (Cookie) Denise, Haley, and Kristy enjoying the sun outside.

K106 Radio broadcast in McComb, Mississippi.

Arrived at K106. Preparing for radio talk shows to air in McComb, Washington, and California.
Thanks to Carl Lazenby.

Radio talk show in McComb, Mississippi. Many thanks to Fern Crossley, a talk show host.

Wallace Allen a California radio talk show host. Broadcasting from McComb, Mississippi to California, and Washington DC revealing a family secret.

Black History Gallery, Inc. 819 Wall St. McComb, MS.
Showcasing African American works.
Many thanks to Ms. Hilda L. Casin.

In the Museum, author found her second edition, "Secrets
Uncovered, J Edgar Hoover Passing For White?"

Millie and big sister Queen visiting the street where she lived before The Projects.

The Projects in McComb, MS.
C4 Apartment 1 Utopian Homes.
The apartment the Author grew up in.

Burglund High School, where Millie graduated, now Higgins Middle School.

Reacquainting with teacher Mrs. O'Neal and her husband, classmates Percy Robinson, Regina Johnson, sister Queen, and friend Edith Moore Patterson.

Cousin's Forever!
Millie and Kristy

Looking at more photographs in McComb, Mississippi.

The Mississippi Trip! "Hello, Lucius Bowser."
Always reading. - New Orleans, Louisiana.

Good friends! What a great Journey! April 8-14, 2002.

Mom's here. The ending to an exciting trip! Many thanks to Pastor, Nathan Johnson of Maranatha Bible Church in McComb, MS.

Saving the best for last! The Author's lover, best friend, and husband Dr. Leslie L. Morris.

ACKNOWLEDGMENTS &
SPECIAL THANKS!

Branden Silks, Steve Marez, Kristy Hoover Sullivan, Haley Sullivan, Queen Ester McGhee, Lucius A. Bowser, Danny Arguello, Jacqueline Groves, Denise Boulden, Mertine Moore, Aaron Brown, Wallace Allen, Tamela Tenpenny-Lewis, Eugene Dillanado, Beverly Brown, James Cotton, Regina Johnson, Nathan Johnson, Jacqueline Martin, George Ott, and Leslie L. Morris, my wonderful husband. Many others who have sent many letters of hope, as well as encouragement.

Mayor, J.C. Woods, Mayor, Robert Bowser, Mayor, Glenn Cunningham, Mayor, Jim Dailey, Governor, Mike Huckabee, Judge, Jack Jones, Mayor, William Alexander.

Thanks to you all. This book is alive because of you, and many others that I met across the country over the last three years.

We recommend you read, No, I Won't shut Up, by Rev. Dr. Barbara A. Reynolds, J. Edgar Hoover, The Man And The Secrets, by Curt Gentry, FBI Secrets, An Agent's Expose, by M. Wesley Swearingen, and Patricia W. McGraw, Ph.d.,wrote Hush! Hush!, Somebody's Calling My Name.

"Thank God For The Good In Many People!"
-Millie L. McGhee

Grandparents of the Author

In Memory of
Big Daddy and Big Mama
Clarence and Lydia Allen

Author, Millie L. McGhee
17 years old

BURGLUND HIGH SCHOOL
Twenty-Fourth Annual
Commencement Exercises

Dedicated to my teacher,
Mrs. O'Neal
Class of 1965

May 20 — June 2, 1965
Burglund High School Gymnasium
McComb, Mississippi

June 2, 1965

Graduated Illiterate!

Reading on a six grade level.

"Dreams do come true."

UNIVERSAL CHILD

*What did you call me? A Universal Child!
What does that mean?*

Yes, my hair is straight, and my skin is dark! My mother is white, and my father is black!

I was born in Louisiana. That's right! The South!

A place where most people have a lot of respect, and hospitality for all creeds and colors.

If you come a little closer, you'll find that my eyes are green, now tell me what does that mean?

I am not ashamed of who I am, or where I came from. No matter what you say I am!

You see, I was taught that character makes a person, and color, doesn't make a man or woman.

You know what? If you take a closer look into the mirror, you may discover, that you too are a Universal Child...As a matter of fact, I'm glad I'm a Universal Child.

A Universal Child is a part of God's Divine Paradise!

By Millie L. McGhee

Millie M.

The Author